Progressive Farmer.

HaNDY DEVICES
For Farm & Home
Edited by Vernon E. Miller

Oxmoor House, Inc. • Birmingham

Library of Congress Catalog Number: 78-55329
ISBN: 0-8487-0487-8

Manufactured in the United States of America
First Printing

Handy Devices For Farm & Home

Managing Editor: Ann H. Harvey
Manuscript Editor: Lane Powell
Editorial Assistant: Nita Robinson
Designer: Pat Holland

CONTENTS

Editor's Note

Although you may not be able to pound a nail straight or be interested in doing the simplest repair job around the farm or home, you will find this book appeals to your tinkering instinct. If you're looking for faster, easier, better ways of doing the dozens of different jobs that need doing around your place or if you want to adapt an item on the market to fit your particular needs, you'll get inspiration that may spur you on to even greater achievements.

But no matter how you classify yourself, you'll marvel at the great things skilled and inventive people do. Each of the ideas in this book came from an individual who actually thought up the idea and carried it out with finesse or from a person who recognized the worth of someone else's idea.

Each of these items was originally published in the "Handy Devices" column of *Progressive Farmer* magazine. You may note that some items presented as home-built devices are available from local merchants. In some cases this is because the idea proved so valuable that production and marketing of a commercial version were undertaken. In other cases, this is because the builder chose to engineer his own version of a product to save money, to incorporate changes in the design, or simply because he wanted to make something with his hands.

We don't expect you to follow any of these ideas to the letter because this isn't a basic how-to-do-it book. But if you do attempt to do so, we caution you to guard all moving parts just as you would be required to do if you were building the item for sale. We urged precaution in both the building and use of all machinery and suggest that you seek competent technical and safety advice in all your endeavors.

Vernon E. Miller

Chapter I

GATes & Fences

Latches & Hinges

■ Remote-controlled door opener works either automatically from an electric timer or by pushbutton. It makes use of a solenoid from an old automatic clothes washer to pull latch at desired time to turn cattle out.

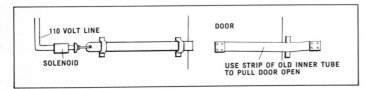

■ A hook on a short length of chain fastened to line post is always handy for holding heavy gate open, and it eliminates time lost hunting for a prop.

■ Tie-rod ends from junked cars make good gate hinges. They are strong and, with grease fittings, they allow easy operation and will last indefinitely.

■ Latch handle, made of a heavy iron rod bent at right angles, hangs down by its own weight and securely hooks into the slot on the gate. This slot is formed in a piece of heavy angle iron bolted to the gate. Edges are beveled for safety.

■ This sturdy gate latch is made of welded rod that slips through short sections of pipe. It is suitable for either single or double gates.

■ Here is an easy-opening latch for wire gates.

When outside loop is pushed down as far as it will go, latch is locked so cattle or horses cannot flip it open. When released, the small inside loop can be slipped up over gate post and the gate pulled open.

Fastener can be built of ¼- x ¾- or 1-inch strap iron. Dimensions can be varied. One lag screw holds fastener to fence post; loose fit is needed so latch may be raised and lowered as necessary.

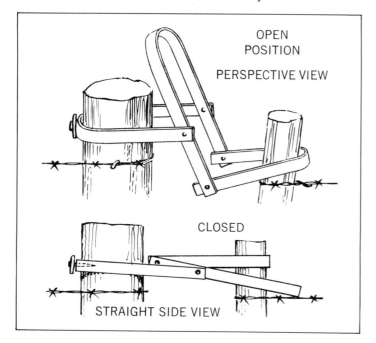

OPEN POSITION

PERSPECTIVE VIEW

CLOSED

STRAIGHT SIDE VIEW

■ This gate latch drops into position by itself when you guide it, then locks itself. Cut slot in gatepost just large enough for bolt made of ½-inch rod. Guide and locking ears on end of bolt are welded in place.

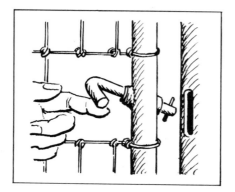

■ Stout stick on a piece of chain is all that is needed to keep gap of hog yard tightly closed. Chain is fastened about 4 inches from end of 2-foot long stick. Other end is fastened to fencepost.

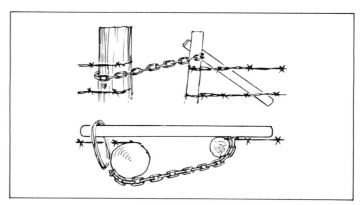

■ This gate is designed so a horse cannot open it. It features a sliding bar latch with a handle that must be turned up exactly 90° before the latch can be moved. In addition, there are spring-loaded safety latches at top and bottom that must be unlatched separately. When the gate is being closed, these latches ride up on the angle iron catch bracket and are then forced back down by the spring when the latch is in line with the catch.

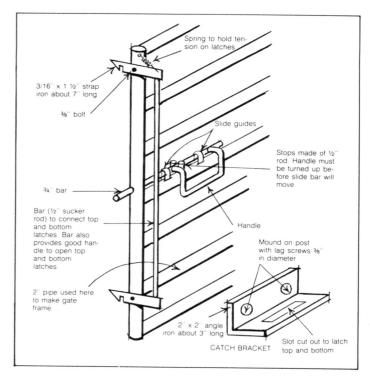

Spring to hold tension on latches

3/16" x 1 ½" strap iron about 7" long

⅜" bolt

Slide guides

Stops made of ½" rod. Handle must be turned up before slide bar will move

¾" bar

Bar (½" sucker rod) to connect top and bottom latches. Bar also provides good handle to open top and bottom latches

Handle

Mound on post with lag screws ⅜" in diameter

2" pipe used here to make gate frame

2" x 2" angle iron about 3" long

CATCH BRACKET

Slot cut out to latch top and bottom

■ A ⅜- or ½-inch rod bent as shown makes it easy to pull a wire gate tight. The large loop is hooked around the gatepost, the rod pushed back, and the end hooked under a strand of wire. The chain permits adjustment should the wire stretch after a period of time.

■ A sliding iron rod that telescopes into a pipe which guides it into place is handy for working and holding pens. The U-shaped handle makes it easier to hold and keeps it from becoming dislocated.

■ This spring latch catches gate when it's pushed shut from either direction. Six-inch tee handle is welded to plunger made from 12-inch length ¾-inch rod. Tension of 3-inch coil spring can be adjusted by moving collar that holds it in place on plunger. Striker plate is curved to fit round post. Short lengths of pipe are used as guides for plunger. One of these fits inside hole drilled through gate.

■ Bull pen gates that need a heavy latch can use this flat iron plate with a T-shaped bolt. There is no gap or give to the gate. Welding bolt to a chain keeps it always handy.

■ Worn wheel bearings from trucks or tractors make excellent hinges for gates built of used pipe. End-piece of gate is slipped through bearings and bearings are welded at proper place before gate is built. Gate is hung by welding outer case of bearings to gate post. Bearings can be protected from sand and rain by covering with a layer of heavy grease or with flat metal disk.

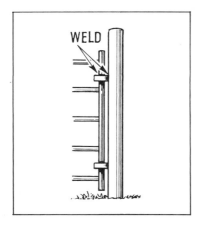

■ Barn door held shut with this latch cannot be opened until piece that locks it in place is swung out of the way.

Exact fit isn't needed, but before permanently fastening lock in place, make sure it swings far enough out of the way to let latch pass. Latch such as this that takes two hands to work will keep one animal from turning another out.

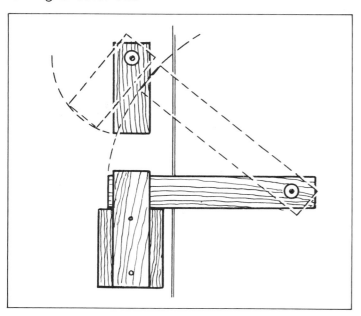

■ Gate hinges of this design can be made as hefty as you want them to be. This hinge is made from pieces of the appropriate-sized pipe and pin welded to ½-inch flat bar iron.

■ This door latch to hold doors open is handier than hooks. To make, weld short length of pipe to U-shaped piece of iron. Drill hole for bolting to building. Off-center weight of pipe holds latch in place.

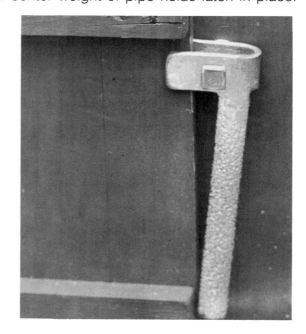

■ Pipe gate covered with steel matting uses a spring latch to make it stay put. The latch is a bent iron rod encased in a compression spring welded on flat iron. A piece of angle iron welded to the gatepost makes an ideal stop.

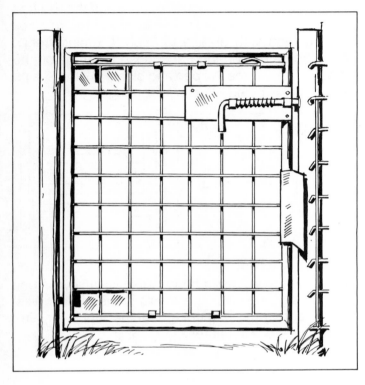

■ Cable neckrails are spring-tensioned and can be tightened with a turnbuckle at each end. The cables slide through short lengths of pipe that are welded to the posts.

Fence Design & Construction

■ To keep electric fence wires from being problems around gates, bury the wire underground. Use single strand underground wire and put it 6 inches or more below the surface so dirt will not wear down to wire. This is much better than running wire overhead, especially when going through gate with a high load.

■ A useful tool for pulling stubborn fence staples is an old square-shanked gate hook. Tap the point in behind the staple to start it; then pry it out, using the leverage you can apply through the long arm of the hook.

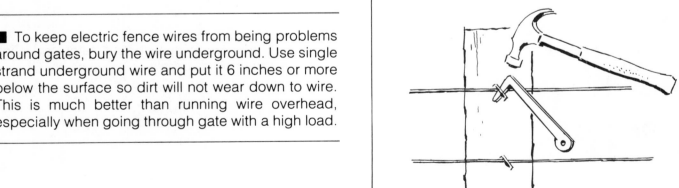

■ Climbing over this fence is easy and safe. The upright is a 3-inch pipe. The foot step is a smaller bar welded through pipe. The short bar welded into the top is to grab as you go over the fence. Low cost and permanent, it doesn't interfere with plowing.

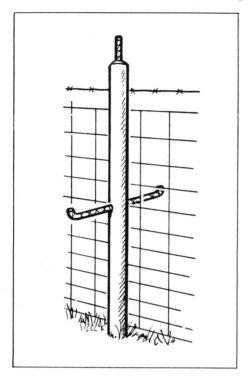

■ Used 1½-inch plastic pipe fastens electric fence to wood posts. Slots to hold wire go halfway through pipe and were cut with a hacksaw.

This idea works well where there are dropoffs in the terrain as shown. It's also good for gaps.

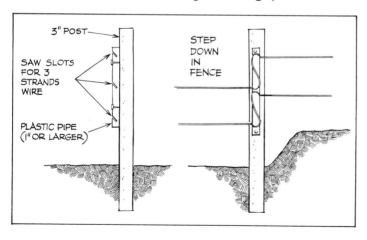

■ Here's a corral fence of pipe and oilfield sucker rods. Ends from the sucker rods made the hinges. The rod box is welded to the end of the gate. The threaded end of a sucker rod is screwed into the rod box from the bottom and then welded to a long bolt. Another sucker rod end is screwed into the top of the rod box to keep out rain and dust. The inside of the rod box may be filled with grease to keep it turning freely. When the gate is opened and closed, it turns on the threads. Gate is free to open and close, but there is no danger of its being lifted off the hinge.

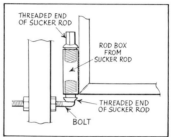
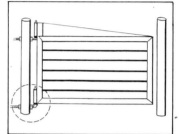

■ A corkscrew of extra-heavy wire with an eye in one end for slipping over the insulator nail is a quick, convenient way of attaching electric fence for temporary livestock pastures.

■ Here, a coil spring between insulator and each corner post keeps wire tight at all times.

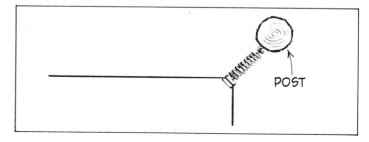

■ This portable fence is built out of 1-inch pipe and ¾-inch oil well sucker rod. It is reinforced with ⅜-inch reinforcement steel.

Each section is 10 feet long and connects to adjoining sections with pins. These pins fit into ½-inch pipe welded on ends of each section. There are 12 sections, so fence size can vary from 10 x 10 feet to 30 x 30 feet.

Two chute sections are made from 2-inch pipe and ¾-inch sucker rod. The work gate is made from 2-inch pipe, 1-inch pipe, and ½-inch angle iron. It can be set at any angle within the portable fence or any other fence, or it can be used as an outside section to the fence.

Entire fence can be loaded on a trailer for moving. It is strong enough to hold a bull, yet each section can be moved by two men.

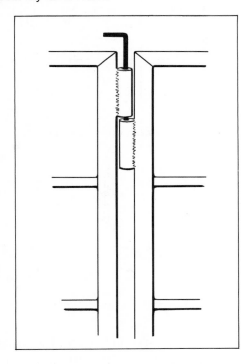

■ Snag-free fence crossing is possible if you put door springs in your barbed wire fence. Springs replace short sections of wire at convenient crossing places.

Gates & Cattle Guards

■ Double gates to this barnlot let cows in with less risk of injury from crowding or butting. Finding a suitable way of latching such a pair of gates is usually a problem. With this latch, gates can be opened by lifting and sliding one long bar.

Gates are built of 2-inch planks. So is the bar which fits between double pairs of uprights on end of each gate and holds both of them rigid when locked. Bar is notched to drop over a cleat on the lower rail. This locks on just one gate but holds both.

■ This gate arrangement for three pastures that join is such that animals can be pastured in almost any combination of pastures desired, as well as transferred from one to the other with a minimum of trouble.

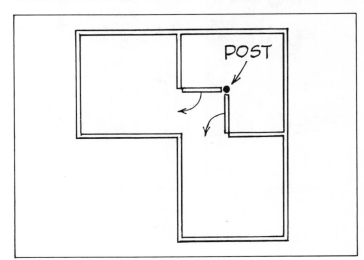

■ Adding a foot or so to the height of a gate may be just what's needed to keep some cattle from going over it. This extension on a feedlot gate is an iron rod bent to the proper shape and welded to the gate framework.

■ Two posts set close together will stop an irate cow but let a workman slip through quickly. Best places for such quick escape openings are along each fence line and in each corner.

■ This gate saves a lot of getting in and out of a vehicle. Just drive up against the gate with the center of the bumper of car or truck against the center of the gate, then shift into low. As the vehicle goes forward, the gate goes over until it lies flat on the driveway. The long board in the center of the gate holds it down until the vehicle is clear of every other part. Gate automatically returns to its upright position when the center board is cleared.

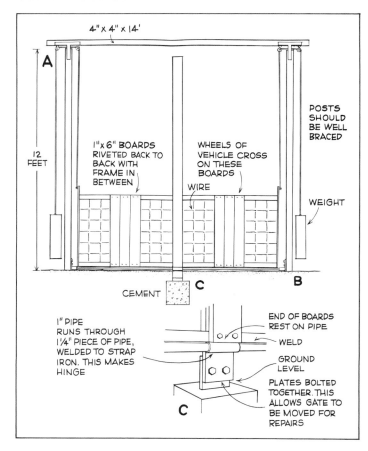

■ Swinging gate is especially good for cattle lots— just pull it one way and step through without any worry about closing it. Livestock do not go through.

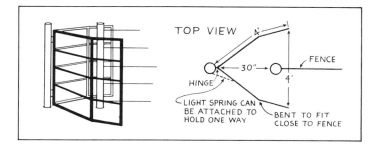

■ Squeeze-gate with locking arm cuts down on excitement and injury to animals that must be confined for treatment. It also protects people handling animals.

Gate can be pushed forward to quietly and gently squeeze animals into position. When animal pushes against gate, locking arm wedges tightly against curved concrete wall built along path of gate and keeps gate from going back toward handler.

A piece of truck tire fastened to a metal plate on end of gate-locking mechanism contacts wall and keeps gate from slipping. Ordinary screen door spring holds arm in position so rubber end stays in contact with wall. Gate can be released by pulling on arm lock rather than gate.

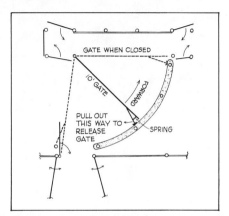

■ Main frame of this gate is 1-inch pipe. Triangular pieces of heavy sheet steel welded in each corner along with a ⅜- or ½-inch iron rod welded diagonally corner to corner make the gate almost sag-proof.

Barbed wires wrapped around the free end of the gate and back to eyebolts in the ¾-inch pipe about 6 inches from the hinge end of the gate complete the enclosure. Bolts at the top and bottom of the ¾-inch pipe keep the wire under tension.

Hinges are made of link sections from a discarded flexible drag. A piece of ¼- x 1-inch strap iron bent to a C-shape and welded to the section link forms the base for each hinge. Open eyebolts through each end of the link and a piece of strap iron on the opposite side of the gate post hold the gate in place. A heavy washer held in place by a bolt above the lower hinge link keeps the gate at the correct level.

The double gates shown are locked in a closed position by a 30-inch length of pipe bolted to one gate and locked in angle-iron brackets by two pins in the other gate. Slots in the pipe supports allow vertical adjustment when lining up the pipe to fit between the brackets. The pins are chained to the gate to prevent loss when they are not in use.

■ This sorting gate, made of welded pipe and hung on 2- x 6-inch crosspieces between posts, can turn cattle as they come from the working chute. The lightweight gate pivots easily on the crosspieces.

■ This extendable gate uses 1¼-inch pipe for the main frame and 1-inch pipe for the extendable portion. The gate is 8 feet 3 inches long at minimum length. It can be extended to 12 feet and still maintain rigidity. It works well in holding areas for mature cattle where driveways of different widths meet.

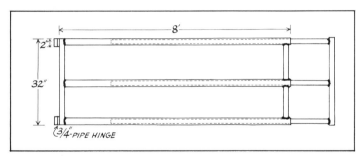

■ Here's a new twist on sliding gates for wide openings. Front end of the gate rides on a pair of wheels spaced and braced to keep the gate upright and off the ground. The rear of the gate is supported by a single wheel rolling in a wide piece of channel iron. Posts alongside the channel iron help hold the gate upright and keep the area clear so it can be opened. The gate framework is of heavy angle iron with cross braces to make it rigid. Chain link mesh fencing covers the framework.

■ Welding an underground crossbrace to gate posts results in a gate that resists movement in any direction.

Posts do not have to be set in concrete. The underground crossover pipe resists movement perpendicular to the line of fence. Note also that this method eliminates need for two additional posts and crossbraces you'd usually have.

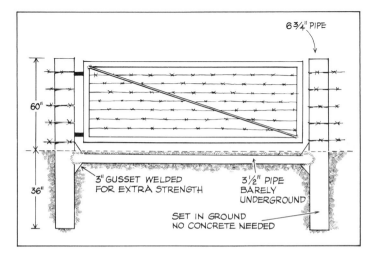

■ Concrete blocks, set holes-up in a shallow pit, form this cattle guard. Floor of pit is covered with bricks, but this foundation could also be built of concrete. There's an extra gate to one side of the cattle guard for moving cattle into or out of the pasture.

■ Leaf from old auto spring arranged in this manner is sturdy enough to close corral gates made of welded pipe.

■ This cattle guard has wings of welded pipe. The far side is boxed in so the lane can also be closed off with a gate.

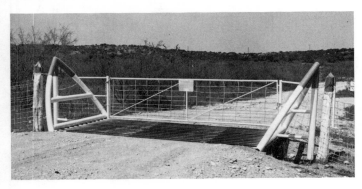

■ This "pasture creep" lets calves on temporary grazing or keeps them off as you choose. Oblong frame of rough lumber just large enough for calves to pass through is tied in place between fence and partly opened gate. When not in use, it is tied to fence near the gate.

■ No matter what material you use to make cattle guards—2 x 4's on 4- x 6-inch stringers or 4-inch pipe on 8-inch well casings—you'll need a way to keep stock from slipping between the guard and the fenceline post. Here are some ideas that you can adapt for your own situation.

Strands of barbed wire tied to the ends of the guard and to the fencepost are quick and inexpensive.

Wheel of a dump rake or horse-drawn cultivator leaned over the line post is attractive as well as practical.

Tractor tire or large truck tire makes an effective barrier when centered against the line fence.

Wire Handlers

■ With this fencing machine two men can string as much woven wire fence in a day as can six men without the machine. Framework is of welded pipe. It fits tractors with three-point hitch. Spike prongs on lock bar (arrow) go through mesh to keep wire from unrolling while stretching fence with tractor. Hydraulic lift keeps wire at right height. New roll of wire is easily slipped into place by pulling out piece of pipe that goes through center of roll.

■ An 80-pound roll of barbed wire can be transported and unrolled with ease with this homemade cart. Three wheels from old push-type lawnmowers are used. The roll of wire rests upon the third wheel and allows it to unroll as needed. Framework is made from ½-inch pipe.

■ This device to roll up and store electric fence takes hard labor out of a time-consuming job. A 2-inch angle iron makes the frame for the 5- x 5-foot platform. For the roller shaft weld a p.t.o. adapter on a 2-inch pipe. Be sure to shield properly. Base for the roller lifts off easily, so the platform is available for many different uses.

■ Differential of an old car is the basic part of this p.t.o. attachment to roll up wire. Operator can roll up two strands of 1,200 feet each, or more, without leaving the tractor. Entire unit is mounted on the three-point hitch.

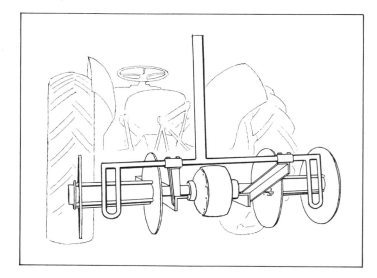

■ This barbed wire holder slips into and out of brackets of 1½-inch pipe on back of pickup so that it can be easily stored when the job is finished. Upright piece of spool holder is 1-inch pipe. Crosspiece at bottom of spool is ½-inch pipe shaped in the form of an "L" to hook over edge of truck bed and keep the entire holder from turning. Spool sits on circular piece of flat steel welded to crosspiece.

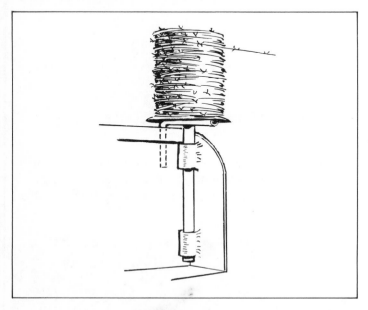

■ Here's a wire roller made from a discarded auto rear end and an old peanut stack puller. It's driven from the tractor p.t.o. When in use, attach an 8-inch length of chain to the loose end of the wire to give it some drag and make it roll up evenly.

■ Fence unroller and stretcher pays out barbed wire as well as woven wire. For stretching, fence is held with angle-iron clamp fastened to the rear frame.

■ Clamp for wire fence stretcher is made from two pieces of 2-inch angle iron, each 45 inches long. Flathead bolts are used to hold fence clamped between nested angles. Cut lengthwise slots in one of angles with larger opening in middle for nut to slip through. The two pieces can then be separated by loosening the two nuts instead of unthreading them all the way.

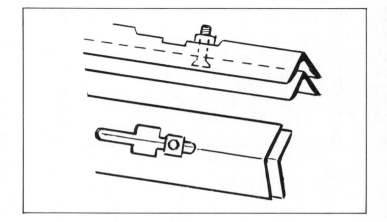

■ This protective shield made of ½-inch plywood prevents injury when stretching fence. If a wire slips out of the clamp, it will be thrown against the shield with great force.

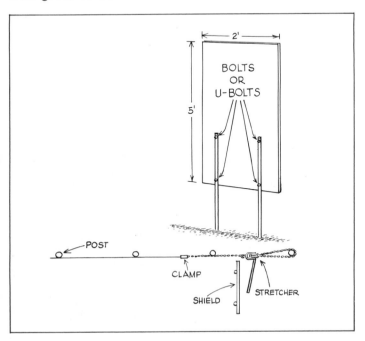

■ Tightener for fence on metal gate is made of four 3-inch bolts and length of iron pipe short enough to fit inside frame of gate. Wire is stretched between this pipe and endpiece of gate, then tightened as needed by running nuts farther onto bolts.

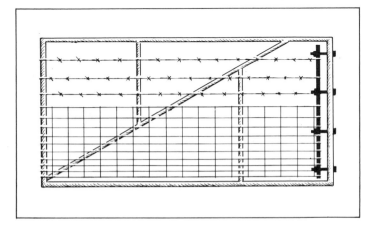

■ Coil springs from automobile keep cable fence tight. One end of spring is welded to corner post and the other end is welded to short post that slides back and forth as animals push against wire rope. Fence is tightened in warm weather and stays tight the year-round. No repairs or upkeep have been needed in over a year. Fence around feedlot has five strands.

Posts & Post Pullers

■ This range fence uses old telephone crossarms (complete with glass insulators) for posts. Because of the insulation at each post, it can easily be converted to an electric fence.

■ To drive metal fenceposts, cap a 3-foot length of 3-inch pipe. Slip this over the post and then use it to hammer post into ground.

■ A platform mounted on back of tractor, normally used for hauling feed and hay, also can be handy for fencing jobs. Haul posts and wire to the fencing site on this platform; then use the platform to stand on while driving posts. This is much easier than standing on the ground because you are higher than the posts.

■ Posts for the feedyard are made of heavy pipe in concrete foundation. A single strand of plastic-covered cable working over two pulleys at the opposite end of this winch keeps the stock from climbing out over the feedbunks. A chain link splice, welded to the intermediate posts, serves as a guide to keep the cable in place. Heavy spring of the type used on overhead garage doors spliced in the cable keeps the tension yet allows some give if the cattle crowd each other.

■ Stump puller made from scrap metal works well for uprooting posts and small stumps. Puller hooks to back of tractor and works off power lift. To use, back up to stump so foot of puller is pushed into and partly under stump. A "V"-shaped slot in foot grasps stump the same way a claw hammer grasps nail. Tractor is kept in reverse as stump is raised by pushing and lifting action.

Shank of puller is a 1- x 5-inch beam 2½ feet long. At upper end is hitch assembly. At bottom is welded the slotted foot made from 6- x 9-inch steel plate, ¾-inch thick. Crossmember of 2-inch angle welded to beam attaches to drawbar to complete three-point hitch.

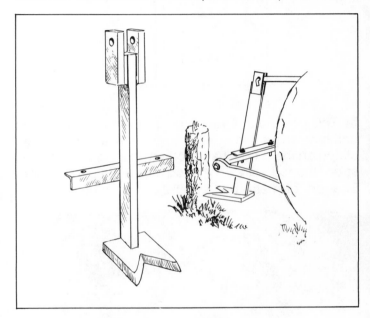

■ To pull fence posts, use a toothed ring attached to a tractor boom. The ring is made from ¾-inch rod, welded to form a 9-inch diameter ring. The teeth are points of old sickle bar knife section. This assembly takes a positive grip on the post while being pulled, then releases the post readily.

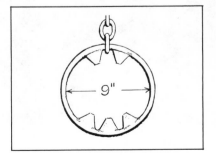

■ Three-eighths-inch reinforcement rod can be used for posts to put up temporary electric fence. Each post is 4 feet long. A nail welded to each one holds an insulator after the post is in the ground. These posts can be driven into ground that's too dry and hard for digging postholes.

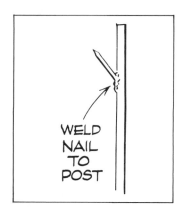

WELD NAIL TO POST

■ This post hole digger uses a gear box from an old combine and a 7-inch seed auger from an old gin. Slip clutch on the p.t.o. shaft protects the digger. Boom is strengthened with 1-inch rod welded along the top. Spacers of metal plate are about 4 inches wide.

■ Just back into a post and raise this puller at the same time to remove wood posts. Puller can also be used as a rock hauler.

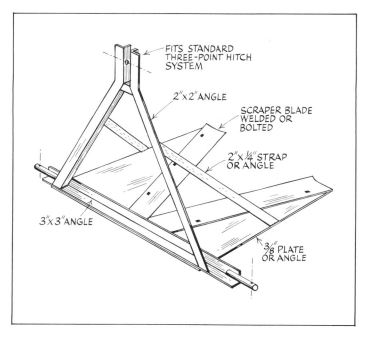

FITS STANDARD THREE-POINT HITCH SYSTEM

2"x2" ANGLE

SCRAPER BLADE WELDED OR BOLTED

2"x¼" STRAP OR ANGLE

3"x3" ANGLE

⅜" PLATE OR ANGLE

■ Dirt tamper built for setting fenceposts has moon-shaped foot so it fits close around posts. Size is ½ x 2 x 4 inches. Handle is 6-foot length of 1-inch pipe. For impact, there's an 18-inch length of 1½-inch pipe that slides up and down on handle. Bottom strip is a collar welded in place about 2 feet from top of handle.

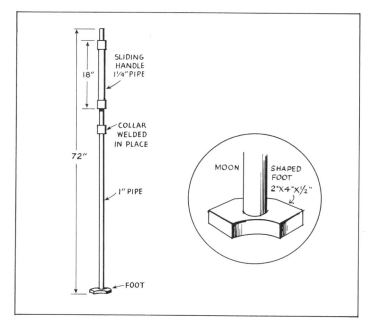

SLIDING HANDLE 1¼" PIPE

18"

COLLAR WELDED IN PLACE

72"

1" PIPE

MOON SHAPED FOOT 2"X4"X½"

FOOT

■ This device will pull up fenceposts without breaking them, by guiding the chain straight upward as tractor pulls at low speed. Place the tool, as shown in the illustration, at an 80-degree angle against the post to be lifted. Attach the chain at ground level around the post and run it through the gap at the top of the device.

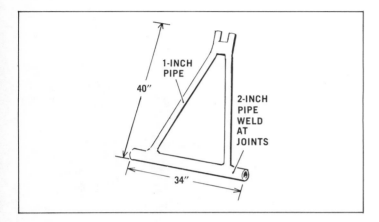

■ Tractor-mounted fencepost puller takes a lot of the work out of removing old fences.

In operation, the jaws of the puller clamp onto the post when the operator actuates a self-centering hydraulic piston.

Then he raises the hydraulic toolbar of the tractor to lift the post.

Working parts of the pole puller are mostly made of ¾-inch steel plate.

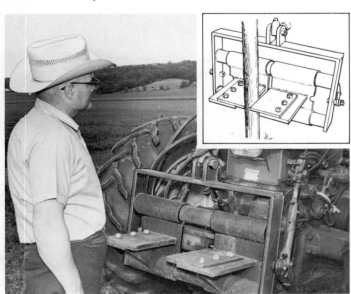

■ This attachment to a post hole digger eliminates the need of a helper while digging holes in hard soil. Just weld a bracket to the post hole digger frame and make a bracket to bolt to the back of the tractor. These brackets have pins to accommodate a standard hydraulic cylinder.

When weight is needed, lower the digger and use the cylinder. Put the cylinder in float position when raising the digger.

■ Portable post is made by pouring concrete in a truck tire and setting post in the center. It has many uses and is easily moved by tipping to a 45-degree angle and rolling the tire. Here it is being used for electric fence separating dry cows from rest of herd.

Chapter II

animaL & crop HanDLing

Chutes & Headgates

■ Height of this portable chute can be varied to match that of the truck bed by raising ramp with a hydraulic jack mounted on the axle. Telescoping pipes at the high end of the ramp are let down for braces.

■ A two-level stock chute, normally used for loading or unloading trucks of 1½- to 5-ton size, can be quickly converted to pickup height by removing one section of chute floor, as shown in sketch. This top-level floor section weighs from 60 to 80 pounds.

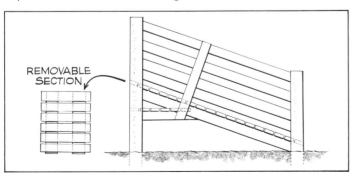

REMOVABLE SECTION

■ Cleats on walkway prevent slipping when you need to get up on the chute to prod animals. Steps built into sides of chute are an added convenience and safety factor.

■ Ladders on each end of chute make it easy to reach over the top of the chute sides when loading or unloading truck.

■ This portable loading chute can be raised from 20 inches above the ground to 7 feet 6 inches.

The axle was from a haybaler with small wheels. Two-inch pipe attached to the axle runs three-fourths the remaining length of the chute. Another 2-inch pipe is used to form the tongue. An iron rod or pipe fits through a hole in the tongue and is welded to the two longer pipes so the tongue will swivel up and down. The hitch can be removed by removing the pin nearest the body of the chute.

Two 4- x 4-inch angle irons are welded upright to the axle. Notches are cut with a torch in the positions shown.

A cable runs from one angle iron, under the chute, to a winch on the other angle iron. When the chute is raised by the winch, a rod ¾ inch or larger is run under the wooden chute through the notches. This takes strain from the cable. Braces go from angle irons to axle and two long pipes.

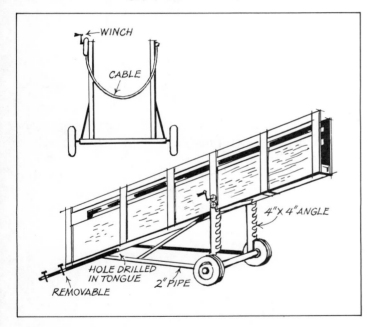

■ A sure-footed loading chute can be made by cutting away sidewalls from old tractor tires and nailing treads flat on the loading ramp.

■ This movable loading chute is mounted on 4 x 6 skids which are faced with iron. Overall length is 14 feet. The cleated ramp is 34 inches wide. Posts are 4 x 4's. There's a catwalk on the side. The chute is easily pulled with a tractor.

■ Height of ramp on this hog-loading chute can be raised or lowered to match floor height of the truck. Free end of the ramp is counterweighted by a pair of nail kegs filled with sand or concrete. These are suspended by cable which passes over pulleys mounted on tall posts of the chute. Hinged plank closes the space between truck bed and ramp. Hinge is made of strap iron wrapped around hinge pin of pipe.

■ This loading chute has covered sides and top to keep the area dark and protected. If the livestock cannot see movement outside of the chute, they are not so apt to spook and try to turn back. And they head for light at end. The fold-down section in the chute is used to load the upper deck of trucks hauling hogs or sheep. It is held up on one side until needed.

■ This blocking gate in the cattle-working chute latches as it is swung behind cattle and also when it is swung out of the chute. It is made of pipe, and slides between guides of heavy angle iron mounted on opposite sides of the chute.

■ Exit ramp from this dairy barn is useful as a loading chute. Elevated part of ramp just outside exit door of barn is correct height for loading trucks. Simply hinge the first panel of ramp fence so it can be used as a gate. Latch is on end closest to barn. To load cows as they come out, swing panel in to close off ramp and funnel animals right into truck without exciting them.

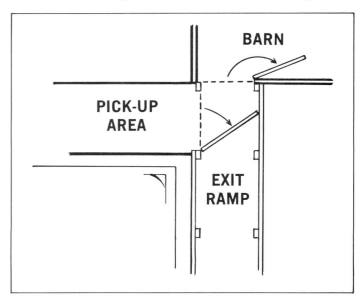

■ Loading dock gates on this cattle chute are connected by a rod and spindles so gates move together. This facilitates lining up rear of truck with loading dock. Gates are latched with a long rod hook that drops into one of a series of holes in angle iron on right side.

■ Lightweight is really the mark of this portable chute because, except for the plank ramp, it is made of aluminum. It is made of aluminum sheets on the side, square pipe uprights, and I-beams for the underneath supports mounted on the axle of a junked car. Adjustable jacks at the high end hold it level when loading animals. A trailer hitch is on the lower end of the ramp. It is bolted together.

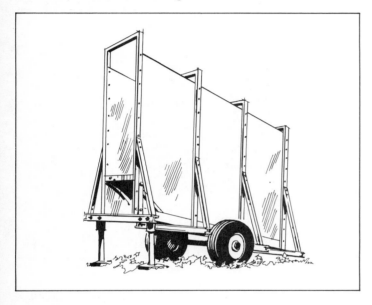

■ Well pipe set in concrete can be used to build this loading chute. The pipes were cut, welded, and flared to widen the chute from 30 inches at the ramp to 40 inches at the top. Channel iron was used for bracing, and plank steps were bolted to heavy angle iron rails to form the ramp floor. Steel matting makes up the side walls.

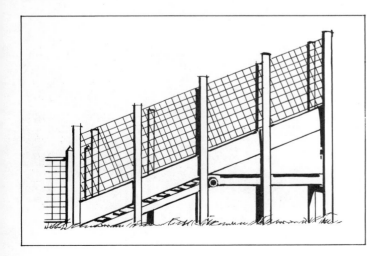

■ Ramp on this chute can be raised to match that of the truck bed, then latched at that place. Chute is made of pipe. Sides are partly covered so animals can't see out and so they can't get legs caught between the rails.

■ Loading trucks with beds of different heights at livestock chute is no problem with this ramp that can be raised or lowered to the right height. It has barn door hinges in the middle and folds for use as a gate.

Ramp is held at right height for truck by iron rod props shoved in holes bored in 2 x 6 uprights, at center and front of chute.

■ Stanchion of this hog-catching crate is opened and closed by overhead notched handle. Closing it draws both sides together by action of the chain which passes over the pulley shown on left side. Opening stanchion by hand-lever likewise spreads stanchion by chain action. Chute is built with sloping sides on the "squeeze" pattern to limit side movement of hog. It is mounted on skids.

■ A headcatcher and chute, built with black pipe and angle iron, has swinging gates at the rear so it can be mated to gates of varying sizes—up to 6 feet in width. Each swinging gate is full width of chute, so gate can be closed from either side.

The chute has a 2-inch oak floor and can be put on runners to be moved wherever wanted. Pipes can slide through holes in flat steel on the sides to keep animals from trying to jump out the top or back up.

■ This split-level loading chute has walls of concrete block. Gentle curves aid in moving cattle by preventing bottlenecks at corners. Design is such that cattle can't see the truck to shy away from it until they're within a few feet of it. Then they're crowded on by cattle behind them that can't see the truck.

Other features of the chute are a diverting gate hinged to the dividing wall and an outside catwalk.

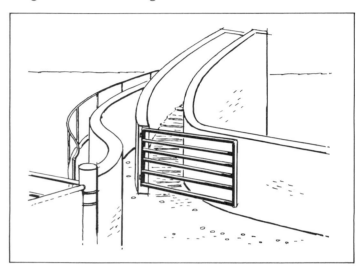

■ Nonslip ramp floor is made by lapping edges of 2 x 8's instead of laying them flat and edge to edge. Chances of loosening and pulling up are lessened by extending ends of 2 x 8's beyond boards that form sides of chute.

■ Ramp on this loading chute can be set at four different levels to match truck bed. Hinged end of the ramp is supported by a length of pipe that drops into cutaway slots of angle irons fastened to chute posts. Ramp is counterweighted by cable, overhead pulley, and a 5-gallon bucket of ballast. Overlapped 2- x 8-inch lumber provides nonslip surface for stock going up the ramp.

■ Here is a cattle holding chute made from old grader blades and boiler pipe. Two-inch pipe works even better.

■ This portable loading chute was built on an old auto frame. Two-inch water pipe or angle iron could also be used to make the frame. The chute is 32 inches wide and 8 feet long. The axle is made from 2-inch pipe. High end of chute is 42 inches from the ground; sides are 40 inches high.

There is a 12-inch spacer between axle and frame. This is braced with ¾-inch pipe extending from axle to frame on each side. Props made from ¾-inch pipe welded to gate hinges tilt the chute. The props fold up and hook to axle for transportation. Chains keep props from slipping out behind.

An extension of the floor folds down to cover tongue for loading and folds back into chute for transportation. The tongue is 2-inch pipe, and a pin through a hole in it forms the hitch. Low end of chute is 6 inches from the ground. Floor and side racks are creosoted oak lumber.

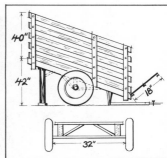

■ This "cow catcher" is made of 2-inch pipe. Spindles for the wheels are from an old car. Two-inch double-strength pipe is used for an axle. It is about 6 inches from the ground. Floor is made from 2 x 6's.

Tailgates & Endgates

■ This telescoping tailgate can be stored in the front of the truck when not in use. The sliding part of the gate is made of ½-inch pipe. It slips inside the stationary part of the gate which is made of 1-inch pipe.

The gate hangs by three hooks from crosspiece of pipe welded to top of sides of the livestock rack. Hooks are made of reinforcement rod and are welded to each of the three upright pieces of the tailgate—two on the stationary part and one on the sliding part.

Bottom of gate is secured by pin welded to lower end of center post. It fits into hole drilled in floor.

■ Tailgate swung from the top is easily unlatched from the front of the box with this arrangement. Moving lever toward rear drops bar at bottom of tailgate to let the tailgate open when dump box is raised. This is a big timesaver when making silage.

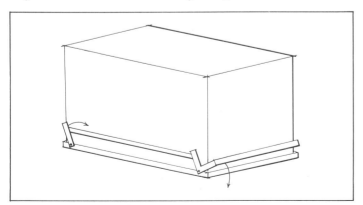

■ Grain door in tailgate of trailer is easily made with four short pieces of ½-inch angle iron, two 3-inch strap hinges, and two snap hooks. Saw door to any size you want. Angle iron reinforcing will make tailgate nearly as strong as it was before sawing. Drill holes through angle iron so snap fasteners can be used to hold door shut.

■ Two hinged gates form the endgate on the stock rack of this pickup truck. Each gate is as wide as the tailgate is high. This closes the gap between truck and loading chute when tailgate is down.

Gates fasten to chute posts by chains with harness snaps on the ends.

Sections of the rack are joined at the inside corners by strap hinges. With hinge pins removed, rack can easily be assembled or disassembled by one man.

■ False endgate with a new wrinkle unloads silage fast.

Several 2- x 6-inch boards are attached to cables used to pull load off truck or wagon box. These boards are placed crosswise in the truck or wagon bed, 3 to 4 feet apart. About twice that much cable is left between boards. When cables are hooked to tractor or winch to pull silage from truck, slack cable between boards allows only part of the load to be moved at one time. By the time first part of load has been removed, slack has been taken up in cable and second section starts moving. False endgate comes dragging along after third section to remove last of silage. Endgate can be held upright with skids or cable as shown in sketches.

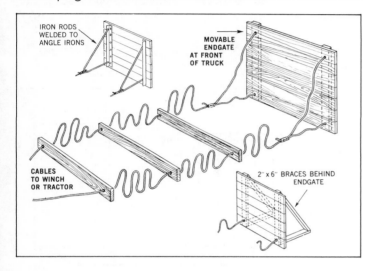

■ Endgates on this portable loading chute let it double as a trailer to move a smaller animal, such as a calf or hog, from one field or farm to another. Wheels and axle came from horse-drawn mower. Endgates are easily taken off.

■ This tailgate for a cattle truck is sturdy and can be opened or closed with truck backed up against loading chute. Sketch shows gate partly open. Slats of left side fit between 2 x 4's with 1-inch spacers. Only one side opens.

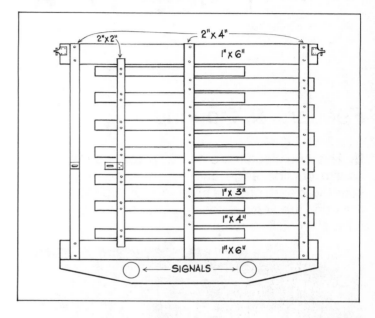

■ This tailgate, built for a stock trailer, will open to either side or drop down so it can be used as a ramp. Use ¾-inch plywood for tailgate and reinforce it with 2- x ⅜-inch flat steel. For ramp hinging, use pipe across entire bottom of tail gate—1-inch pipe inside 1¼-inch pipe. Hinge pins are L-shaped for easy removal.

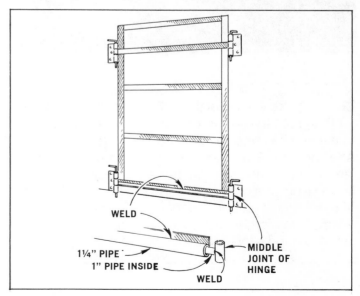

CHAPTER III
LIVESTOCK

Feeders & Troughs

■ This bunk features a cast-in-place rub rail of pipe on the outside edge and an angle iron top on the inside edges to prevent chipping. Outside surfaces of the bunk are vertical. Inside surfaces are rounded to form a smooth curve.

■ Two barrels—one of them 6 inches larger in diameter than the other—can be used for forming concrete to make a salt and mineral feeding box for livestock. After pouring 2 or 3 inches of concrete in bottom of larger barrel, use smaller barrel for inside form and finish filling with concrete. Supports for roof are made of used pipe and set in concrete. Chicken netting is used for reinforcement. Drain is short length of pipe set in place before pouring concrete.

■ This private feeder can help keep a bull in top condition and thereby ensure breeding performance.

The feeder is a small metal pen with separate compartments at one end for ground feed and hay. Removable gate keeps bull in pen during feeding. Entire unit can be easily moved from pasture to pasture.

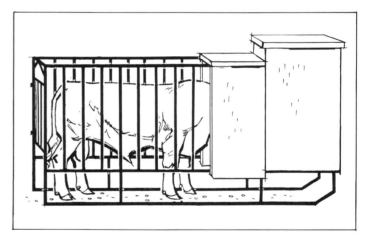

■ Here's a way bucket-fed calves can learn to eat grain quickly: nail an old bucket to the wall or a post in the calf pen and use this bucket as a holder for milk for the calf.

When the calf finishes the milk, take the bucket out and put in grain or pellets. The calf, looking for more milk, soon learns to eat grain this way.

■ To keep birds from eating out of calf feeder, hang small chains over the opening of the feed box. Chains are about 1 inch apart and loose at the bottom end.

■ By mounting inside feedbunks on a short piece of pipe and fitting a 2 x 8 leg at each end to hold it steady, they can be quickly turned over to empty cobs and litter between feedings.

■ Angle iron and pipe are welded to form this four-stall sow feeder. The front end is mounted in two halves of boilers welded end to end. Stalls are 20 inches wide, 33 inches high, 4½ feet long.

■ Adding 3-inch concrete bottom to large tire makes it more suitable for use as feed or watering trough. For reinforcement, drive nails into lower bead and lace with wire.

■ Hay or grain can be fed to dairy calves in this small feeder which hangs on the wall or on a partition. It needs no back. It is framed with 1-x 4-inch lumber with 1-x 2-inch slats. The grain box catches leaf shatterings when feeding hay.

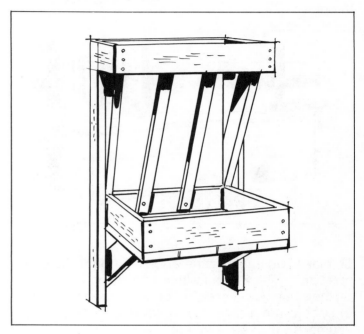

■ A low base and flared sides on this feedbunk make it easy to eat from—it's suitable for cattle of varying ages and sizes. The sides are made of 2-x12-inch planks held together by rods threaded on both ends. The ends are removable, fitted in slots. Legs are framed of bolted dimension lumber, cleated on both sides and bolted to the bunk sides. The floor is made of three 2 x 12's.

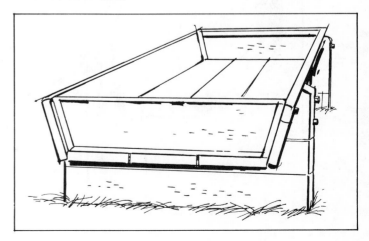

■ A centrally located water tank can serve three or more pastures depending on how you arrange fences. Gates located near the water tank help move cattle from one pasture to another, because they make it easy to corner animals and force them through.

■ Make two salt or mineral boxes from a 50-gallon steel drum. They're cut with an overhang to keep rain off the salt block. A piece of chain welded to the back of each drum makes it easy to tie to a tree or post. Drums are also easy to move. A bar across the front lower side keeps the salt in place. A solid piece of metal welded across the bottom instead of the bar would allow this holder to be used for loose minerals.

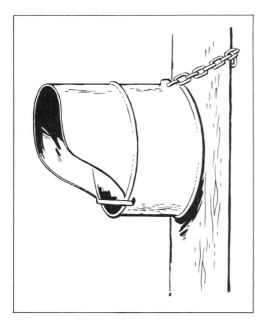

■ This rolling feed rack gets filled at the barn, then towed to cattle.

Old pipe was used for framework of this all-metal rack. Sides are of corrugated metal. Curved sections of sheet metal flooring are hinged in the middle. Props hold floor up in closed position for moving, help support floor when dropped to feeding position. Suspended chains help keep cattle from wasting hay.

■ The size of calf going into this creep feeder can be controlled by adjusting an upright roller pipe at 2-inch intervals. Calves can pass through a space ranging from 14 to 22 inches depending on the adjustment. The feeder is on skids for mobility.

■ Creep feeder built on wagon chassis can be moved easily as you rotate cattle between pastures. It also features a mineral feeder on the back end. This is outside the creep feeder fence so mineral is available to all cattle in the pasture.

■ Metal box set in end of watering trough keeps livestock from ruining float. Hole in end of box lets water into trough. The cover ordinarily remains closed. If needed, posts at each corner will give further protection.

■ This old dishpan with its tire bumper makes an excellent feeder for one large animal or two calves. Even a bull with a long chain hooked to a nose ring cannot turn it over or tear it up.

■ Triangular dolly with swivel casters is welded to milking parlor feed barrel. It holds three bags of feed and can be pushed anywhere about the milking parlor.

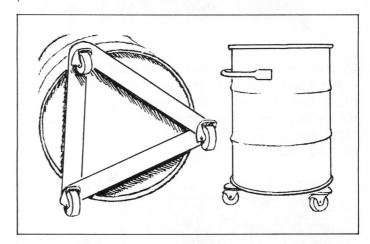

■ Mixing up milk replacer? Use an old-fashioned egg beater or 1-gallon butter churn (first put in the water; then add the milk replacer, and stir). An old agitator washing machine has been used by some. So has a quarter-inch drill. For the mixing tool weld the wheel from a small gate valve, or a small gear, to the end of a quarter-inch rod about 18 inches long.

■ This combined "hover" and creep for baby pigs is built alongside farrowing stalls. Pigs come into this area to nestle in warmth that comes from hot water pipe running through concrete slab floor. They soon begin nibbling on starter from small, galvanized feeder located at end. Hinged top keeps in both heat and pigs.

■ This welded grain and hay feeder for horses or cattle is built with pipe runners. The grain troughs are made from 55-gallon steel barrels split in half. The feeder is framed with iron pipe and covered on the ends with sheet metal. The hay hopper is made of welded rods.

■ Movable concrete feedbunks can double as watering tanks. Sides are flat on the outside but curved on the inside for ease in keeping clean. Moving is simplified by hitching to reinforcing rods at bottom. They protrude in a loop on each side.

■ Both hay and silage can be fed in this feeder made of 55-gallon barrels welded end to end, angle-iron exterior framing, and welded rods. Pipes welded to the underside hold it up off the ground and also serve as runners for moving the feeder.

■ The "drop-in" feature of this salt or mineral feeder makes tray replacement a simple job. All you do is drop in another discarded kitchen sink. Cleaning is also simplified.

The framework is made to fit the standard 30- x 18-inch double sink. Because it's built on a base made from two 36-inch lengths of railroad track, the feeder is not likely to be blown over in strong winds. Yet you can easily move it to a new location by pulling it behind a tractor.

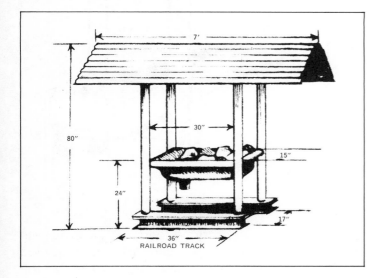

■ Plywood was used to build a poultry feed cart that is powered by a 12-volt battery and a starter from an old automobile. Pushbutton switch to operate cart is on steering handle. Bracket to hold starter is welded to framework behind battery. This three-wheeled cart operates at walking speed and will carry 200 pounds feed.

Guide wheel is from a 28-inch bicycle. Drive wheels have 3.50-12 tires and solid axle. This turns inside bushings made of pipe. These are welded to cart framework, which is built from 1½-inch pipe. Drill holes in bushings so that axle can be kept well greased. Power is transmitted through motor scooter chain. There's a 10-inch sprocket on axle and a 3½-inch sprocket on starter. To keep from damaging starter by overheating, don't keep it in continuous operation longer than two minutes. Battery needs charging once a week or less.

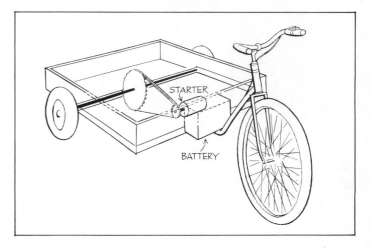

■ Heavy rollers support self-feeding gate for trench silo. Bracket for roller and for hanging gate is built of welded pipe. Cleats on roller keep gate from "inching" back. Short length of heavy strap iron coming down from top of bracket right behind roller also digs into concrete top of silo wall to keep gate in place.

■ Block salt holder is made from an old truck rim. Just weld four pieces of iron—each about 4 inches long—to the top and set salt inside them. Salt absolutely will not fall out and holder will not turn over.

■ Oil barrels cut in half and welded together form the main part of this feedbin. One-half-inch rods welded across the top stiffen the barrels and sides of the bunk made from 2 x 6's.

■ To keep pigs from getting into the trough with all fours and shoving the feed out, build this regular V-shaped trough with extra-long ends. Nail a 1- x 3-inch or 1- x 4-inch board to each end and bore holes every 2 inches in them. A stick running through the holes from end to end across the trough can be adjusted as the pigs grow. The long ends serve to balance the trough.

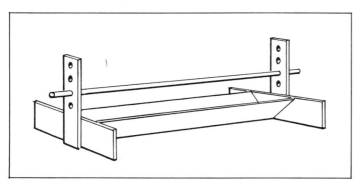

■ This calf feeder for grain, salt, and silage is quickly cleaned by dumping. It rests between the short posts set in the ground and is supported by crosspieces. One leg on each end, made from a piece of a 2 x 6, prevents calves from tipping the trough by raising it with their heads. The trough is made from 2-inch lumber.

■ This horse hay and grain feeder is covered with exterior plywood on the ends and roof. It is 5 feet wide and 16 feet long. Manger slats are 2 x 4's and the full-width bunk is made of 2 x 8's. The framing is made of 4 x 4 posts bolted to 4 x 6 runners.

■ Minerals or salt can be kept dry in this outdoor metal feeder. This box is made of sheet metal and is 12 inches deep, 2 feet wide, and 28 inches high. Curved overhang is 15 inches front to back. It can be bolted to fences, buildings, posts, or hay feeders.

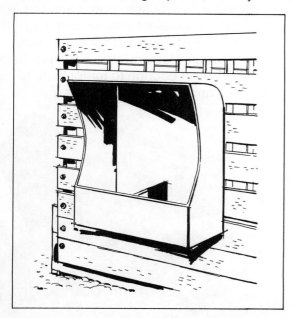

■ An old hot water tank can be used as a hog trough by removing the galvanized tank and cutting it lengthwise. Then weld a piece of scrap iron on each end so it won't roll.

Sprayers, Oilers, & Dusters

■ Here's a low-pressure livestock sprayer that is inexpensive, but effective. It's an old clothes washing machine. Just make a connection for a short length of large-diameter garden hose on the discharge side of the drain pump. You can mix the chemicals right in the tub by using washing action of the machine. A pistol-grip nozzle for garden hose gives good spray control.

■ To keep flies off calves' faces, hang an old tire from a tree limb, wrap with burlap bags, and soak the burlap with oil and insecticide. Calves like to butt the tire and play with it. This gets insecticide on their faces, when they usually don't get it from back oiler. Older cattle sometimes will butt tire, too.

■ Automatic hog sprinkler is adjusted to give hogs a one-minute shower every half-hour. Diagram shows wiring. Electricity is fed through a 15-ampere fuse and then to timer when the on and off time of the shower is adjusted. A 7½-watt bulb is connected to the two wires coming off the timer so you can see when sprayer should be working.

The electrically operated water control valve is from an automatic washing mashine. This has two valves, each opened and closed with a separate solenoid. One was for hot water and the other for cold water; but both were used for cold water and wired so they operate at the same time. That's the reason two hoses are shown on inlet side of valve.

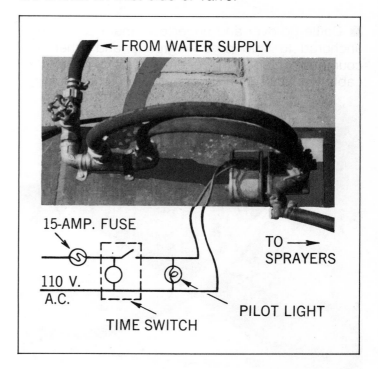

■ Here's an idea for dusting cattle to protect them from flies. Build a 6- x 8-foot shelter with a divider through the middle to form two lanes. Then hang a dust bag on each side. This shelter was built in a lane between two pastures that cows graze each day. So each time they went from one pasture to the other they had to go through the shelter and under the dust bags.

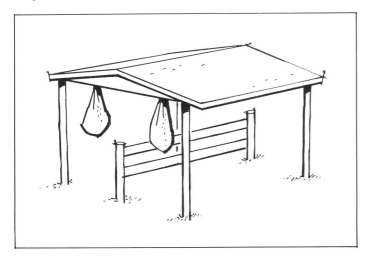

■ Cattle go over and under oiler that has one end anchored to stub post in ground and other end counterweighted with concrete weight on end of cable that passes through pulley on fence post.

■ Oilcans "fuel" this homemade back oiler. Long cans containing insecticide are fastened to each end of 3-inch hemp rope attached to overhanging eaves of mineral feeder.

When rope is slack, cans are vertical and no fly-killer flows. But when a cow raises rope, cans are tipped horizontally and oil flows out through openings at the top. A felt filter keeps it from flowing too fast.

Rope has enough slack so that it covers back of animals well—but not enough to tempt them to reach over instead of under it to get to feed.

■ Hog oiler set at 45-degree angle is more practical than one set straight up and down. Animal can rub its back as well as its sides. If making your own oiler, just wrap several thicknesses of burlap around post set in ground. Keep burlap soaked with oil to help lessen spread of lice and mange.

■ To make this cattle duster, take a 5-gallon can with a flat top and drill a hole in the center of the top and bottom. Then put an iron rod through these holes for an axle on which the can could turn. Use washers as stops to keep the can in the middle of the rod.

With a 16-penny nail, punch holes around the sides of the can, wrap the can with burlap, and fill it with insecticide powder.

Can is mounted on posts so cattle must go under it as they leave the corral. Axle mounts on post are made of strap iron. They have plenty of play so duster rides higher when larger cattle go under, and yet are low enough so it rolls down backs of smaller animals as they go under it.

Since it is mounted low, this duster also keeps horses out of the corral.

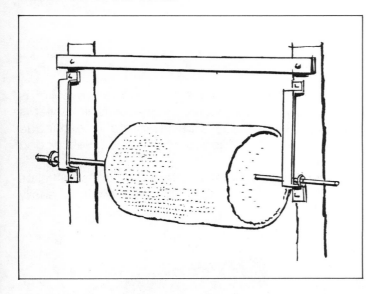

■ When spraying cattle, if you use hot water, you can spray them right out in the pasture. They welcome the warm spray and won't run from it as they do from spray mixed with cold water.

■ Calves dust themselves whenever they go to the feed bunk. Tow sacks filled with insecticide hang from roof covering feed. Plastic film keeps material dry during wet weather.

■ This cattle back-rubber helps control lice. It's simply a piece of 4-inch pipe filled with insecticide and suspended in a doorway. The 30-inch-long pipe is capped at one end and fitted with an elbow and filler plug at the other end. Every time cattle bump it, the insecticide splashes out of ⅛-inch holes spaced every 6 inches along the top, saturating burlap bags that are wrapped around the pipe and tied with baler twine. To "increase the scratch" and encourage cattle to use the back-rubber, wrap barbed wire around the burlap.

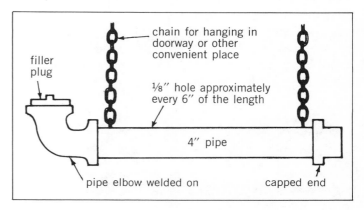

chain for hanging in doorway or other convenient place

filler plug

⅛" hole approximately every 6" of the length

4" pipe

pipe elbow welded on

capped end

Stock Equipment & Buildings

■ This portable livestock retaining table is mounted on a car axle and wheels, and hinged so it can be raised and lowered hydraulically from a tractor. It is raised and cattle strapped to it by belts taken up by a handcrank. The winch has a ratchet and chains attached to the ends of the belts and shaft. The table is 5 x 8 feet and built of 2-inch planks.

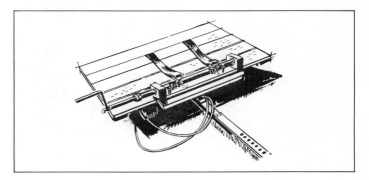

■ Offset scoop mounted on rear of garden tractor effectively and quickly removes droppings under cage layers. Just drive down center aisle to fill scoop, then dump droppings in wagon at end of poultry house.

■ This hog sun shade doubles as a shed—just lower the two sides and one end. It is 5 feet high, 12 feet wide, 20 feet long. Low-pitch gabletype roof is formed by using purlins of different widths fitted lengthwise in pairs on each side of ridge. Hinged sides and end are covered with metal roll roofing. Short lengths of sheet metal roofing cover the top. Pressure-treated lumber will add years to the life of the structure.

■ Here's a simple way to handle your cow-preparation buckets. Strap and snap arrangement keeps buckets off the floor and out of the way. Use three buckets—one for the chlorine water, one for rinsing water, and one for soiled cloths.

■ Branding iron handles don't get so hot when they're made of galvanized pipe. Holes of ¼- to ¾-inch diameter drilled at intervals increase the circulation of air to cool the handle, and they also improve grip.

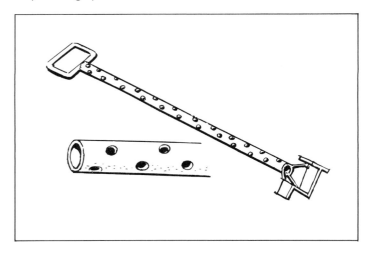

■ Branding furnace made from old range boiler is heated by torch connected to LP-gas tank. Boiler is lined with firepot clay and has grate of expanded metal. Iron rod welded across front gives added strength.

Rack on which handles of branding irons rest slips into pipe nipples welded to pipe, so it is easily movable.

■ For easier loading and unloading of litter in broiler houses, hinge the sides of truck box so they can be dropped down. Also make the tailgate in two pieces.

■ To keep racks from scarring the paint on a new truck, split pieces of rubber hose and nail to the bottoms of the rack.

■ Salvaged furnace fan mounted in plywood frame and on 2 x 4 bracket fits in the farrowinghouse window to provide ventilation for sows.

■ When the pipes have rusted off your metal calf or hog pen, you can reinforce it without chipping away and replacing the concrete to install new pipe. Take the pipe off the top and insert a smaller diameter pipe into the old rusted pipe. Replace the pipe at the top or put on new pipe if needed.

■ To make a hard job easy take along some bathroom scales when checking cows at calving time. Just hold the calf in your arms and step on the scales—then subtract your weight.

■ Trailer and truck bodies lined up near on-the-farm egg processing plant provide ideal storage for cartons and other supplies. In case of fire or breakdown in the plant, supplies could quickly be moved to a neighboring plant.

■ Sliding doors along the back of the pole shed allow cattle to loaf in a cool place. Track on bottom as well as top keeps doors from flapping, even if opened only partially.

■ Heat lamps in farrowing house usually keep pigs warm enough. In case of unusually cold, windy, and rainy weather at farrowing time, give them further protection with a 55-gallon drum. Stand the drum on its open end, cut a small hole in the other end to hold the heat lamp, and cut an opening at the bottom so pigs can get inside.

■ A sheepshed made of metal pipe mounted on skids can be moved from one range to another in a hurry. Pipe is also used for cross bracing to keep it sturdy. One side of the shed is enclosed to serve as a weather break.

■ Portable vacuum pump is a handy piece of equipment around the dairy barn. Wheel it to cows isolated from the herd, and also take it to fairs. It is equipped with vacuum gauge and relief valve, and needs only to be plugged into electrical receptacle.

■ To keep livestock from slipping and injuring themselves when being hauled in the truck, cover the floor with a "checkerboard" made from 1 x 2's nailed on 12-inch centers. Bedding is placed over the checkerboard. When the truck is needed to haul grain, pull the rack out the back. Most of the bedding comes with it, so cleaning the truck takes less time than usual. For trucks over 12 feet long, the rack can be made in two sections.

■ For drenching sick calves, slip an old milk inflation tube over the top of a soft drink bottle. Most calves will grab the rubber tube as they do a nipple and suck contents out of the bottle.

■ When washing cows' udders, protect your sleeves and wrists with a cuff cut from a heavy rubber glove.

■ For a sturdy pail to use in the dairy barn, put a plastic pail inside a galvanized one. Take the handle off the plastic pail. Chlorine and iodine solutions used for washing cows' udders do not affect the plastic.

■ Hoof trimming is made easier by this homemade cattle stock. It is made of 6 x 6 posts well anchored between 2 x 6 runners. The posts are set 30 inches apart (inside measure). Cattle having hooves trimmed can be secured and a knee bent, resting the foreleg on the 2 x 6 rail at the side. Holes in this rail and a 4 x 4 bolted beside it are used for the binding rope. A hand winch controls the belly straps.

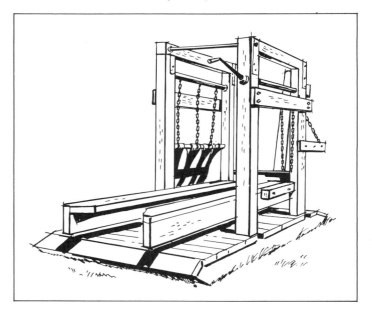

■ Cold water on a freshly branded calf is soothing to burns, and the brand seems to leather over better. Apply with sponge or soft cloth.

■ To light gas brooder stoves, use a welder's spark-lighter. You can get one at most hardware stores. This tool is much safer, easier, and more economical than matches.

■ An engine salvaged from an old haybaler powers this machine for cleaning out chicken houses. Basic framework and power train came from an old automobile. Only the rear wheels were used. The motor was sold and the money used to buy a hydraulic pump. Two boat trailer wheels were used for the tricycle steering. Bucket and hydraulic cylinders came off an old tractor. All welding was done in the farm shop. It can handle larger loads than most factory-built machines.

■ To tattoo cattle without a helper, use a carpenter's apron for holding the tattoo pliers, ink, rubbing alcohol, and other items. They fit nicely in the nail pockets. Apron is suspended by a strap around the neck and waist, leaving both hands free to get calf into the proper position. With calf's head held securely between your knees, you have tools at hand.

When finished, change the tattoo numbers and roll the apron up with the tools inside where they are ready for use the next time.

■ Here's a good way to keep hogs still and comfortable when you're hauling them to market. Buy 100 pounds of cracked ice (large pieces) and throw it in with the bedding in the truck bed.

■ Protect your horse's tender hoof, when trimmed too close, with a felt lining for a cushion between hoof and the shoe to be nailed on. Use the shoe for a pattern by which to cut the lining. The felt need not be new. An old felt hat works fine.

■ Welded step of deck plate and strap iron bolted to side of pickup body is safer to stand on than fender when loading or climbing over stock rack.

■ Overhanging reinforced concrete apron makes manure handling easier. If spreader is parked under apron, manure can be pushed in with blade on tractor.

Chapter IV

machinery & equipment

Tractors

■ This two-wheeled garden tractor was converted to a four-wheeled unit used for mowing. Frame for front wheels is made from two lengths of 2-inch pipe welded side by side. One end of this frame slips inside frame of garden tractor and is fastened with a ⅜-inch bolt.

Crosspiece on which front wheels are mounted also is 2-inch pipe. Welded to center of this crosspiece is a short length of 1½-inch pipe. This slides into one of the pipes that forms frame. It is held in place by a bolt. Bolt hole in frame is slotted to make front wheel assembly flexible and prevent frame twisting when you're traveling over uneven ground. Bumper (not shown in sketch) is welded to this assembly. Hood is cut from an old oil-burning space heater.

Rotary cutting unit is belt powered. It is suspended at the front from tractor frame with a U-shaped hanger. Back end of cutting unit rests on adjustable shoes that slide along ground. Cutting unit can be lifted by raising lever which pivots on tractor frame and is attached to cutting unit with vertical rod. Footrest and front support for seat also are welded to front part of tractor frame. Hitch at rear takes care of two extra self-powered mowing units.

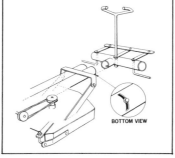

BOTTOM VIEW

■ Reflective paint on an old license plate helps warn motorists coming up behind farm machinery at dusk. Headlights can pick up the reflector as far away as 1,500 feet.

■ This device prevents a tractor operator from being hurt or killed by falling from the tractor seat into the path of towed equipment. Install a jack waist-high on the steering wheel column. The plug that completes the electrical circuit to the ignition system is fastened to the operator's belt with a cord so that it's automatically removed—and the circuit broken—when he gets off the tractor.

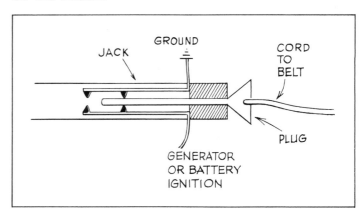

■ Having to stop the tractor, get off, and climb up to see how much fertilizer is left in a pull-type spreader can be annoying. Cut a 6- x 12-inch opening in the center front of the spreader and cover it with a piece of plexiglass bolted in place. Then you can see how much fertilizer is in the spreader without getting off the tractor.

■ This tractor shade is a metal frame covered with heavy duck. It fits in brackets permanently mounted on rear axle housing, but can easily be taken off by one man.

Scrap metal can be used. Keep the shade as light as possible without its being flimsy. Outside of framework, to which duck is sewed with nylon thread, is ½-inch pipe. Crossbracing is 7/16-inch rod. Uprights are 1-inch pipe that fits 8 inches into 1¼-inch pipe of mounting bracket. Collar welded near bottom of each upright is to keep it from slipping too far into bracket.

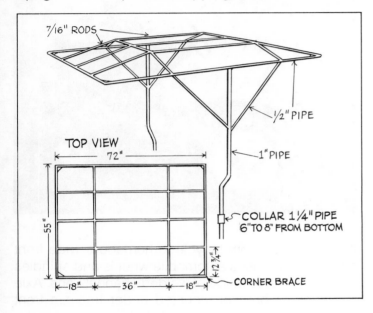

■ Flag on long pole fastened to tractor or self-propelled equipment may save your life. Drivers shooting over slight rise in road can spot flag before they are able to see slow-moving vehicle. Add light on top of pole for safer driving at dusk or in darkness. Flag holder can be made from scrap pipe welded to flat plate that bolts to tractor. Fishing cane makes a good pole. It can quickly be slipped out for passing under low wires.

■ Diesel tractors start more easily on cold mornings when given a boost with heat from the exhaust of your pickup or car. Feed heat into the air cleaner of the tractor through a flexible hose.

■ To insure proper air pressure in tractor tires, buy or borrow a set of steel number stamps and mark proper air pressure near the valve stem on every wheel. Even when the wheel is muddy, only a second is needed to wipe dirt off so the number can be seen.

These numbering sets also are useful to stamp lubrication intervals near fittings or service areas, especially on equipment that is not used often. To help guard against missing any lubrication points, stamp the grease gun bracket of each machine with the total number of grease fittings to be lubricated. Check operator's manuals carefully to be sure of totals before stamping.

■ With these steel wheels, flat tires are no longer a problem when clearing new ground or clipping pastures that contain stobs or thorns. Regular wheels and tires were replaced with steel wheels from which lugs were removed. Then treads from old tractor tires were bolted on.

■ Valve stem guard for tractor tire is a slightly curved piece of steel welded to rim. It is close enough to valve for protection, yet far enough away to leave room for taking off valve cap and inflating tire.

■ To maintain precision in plowing, mount an ordinary household mirror near the front axle of your tractor. A 10- x 14-inch mirror can be mounted with two pieces of angle iron so it's adjustable to any angle. It's easy to use a mirror when going forward—just steer in the direction indicated by the mirror image.

■ As a safety factor, how about a mercury switch designed to cut off motor when front end of tractor reaches a certain height?

■ This tractor was built for mowing the lawn. Engine, steering, and most other parts came from a 1958 Triumph automobile. Frame is made from 3-inch channel iron. Allis-Chalmers mower gets its power from an extra pulley on front of crankshaft. Power for raising and lowering mower comes from hydraulic motor. Power is transmitted from transmission to differential by one to four chain drive gears. Hood and seat were shaped from cardboard and then fiber-glassed to quarter-inch thickness.

■ Conversion from tricycle to homebuilt, wide front end on tractor uses automobile wheels and spindles mounted on axle made of welded channel irons. Axle is pinned to bracket mounted under tractor's front end. A second bracket, slightly behind, supports the wishbone bracing. Steering is through the regular post to a bar connected with the steering assembly.

■ This tractor was built mainly for lawn cutting. It has a 12-horsepower motor. Transmission and steering mechanism came from a pickup. So did front and rear axles, which were cut down to 42 inches for the front and to 44 inches for the rear. Tractor features hydraulic brakes, shock absorber seat, boxed L-iron frame, live power takeoff, and hand lever adjustment of the 42-inch rotary mower.

■ Turnbuckles will hold old tires in place when they are put on tractor to protect good tires while cutting brush. After cutting old tire as shown in sketch, bolt flat steel plates to sides of tire. Holes in plates are keyhole shape for hooking ends of turnbuckles. A heated metal rod will punch holes for the bolts.

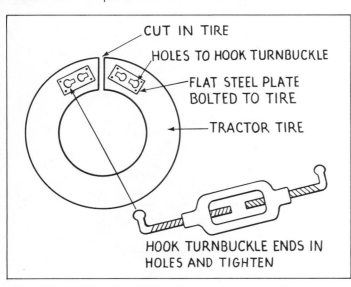

CUT IN TIRE
HOLES TO HOOK TURNBUCKLE
FLAT STEEL PLATE BOLTED TO TIRE
TRACTOR TIRE
HOOK TURNBUCKLE ENDS IN HOLES AND TIGHTEN

■ To get a greater variety of speeds and pulling power from a home-built tractor, mount two 1½-ton truck transmissions in a line behind the engine. For pulling heavy loads, put both transmissions in low.

■ This home-built crawler tractor is good for working garden spots because it doesn't pack the soil down. Tracks are made from tractor tires. To transmit power from drive wheels to track, weld ⅝-inch rods across the rims 6 inches apart. Cleats bolted inside of tractor tire tread are 6 inches apart and fit the contour of the rims. When the wheels turn, one cleat catches the rods as the drive wheel turns. This gives good traction in wet or dry weather. Top speed of this machine is 20 miles per hour. It will pull a 12-inch plow.

Basic parts used to build the tractor were a two-cylinder Wisconsin air-cooled engine, four-speed Dodge truck transmission, Studebaker car differential, and Chevrolet brake master cylinders for steering.

■ For inexpensive tractor wheel weights, visit your farm machinery dealer's junkyard and pick up some old haybaler flywheels. Just cut part of the hub from the flywheel and bore two holes in the tractor wheel.

■ Sides of two hammermill screens welded together and mounted to curve around sides and back of tractor seat give protection to operator from rocks and sticks during mowing with a rotary mower. Holes in the screen allow for viewing to the rear.

Scrapers, Spreaders, & Sprayers

■ Here's how to save bruised hands and skinned knuckles when getting rid of dust and dirt that have gathered in fertilizer distributors over winter. Take a long piece of tarpaulin or tow sacking, and place it lengthwise in the bottom of the hopper directly in front of the drive shaft or fins. Turn the drive shaft by the wheels a time or two. Then remove cloth and shake.

■ This snowscraper mounts on the front of a tractor. The blade was made from an old water tank cut in half lengthwise, straightened a little, and reinforced with leaf springs from an automobile. Plow shares with the ends cut off were used for a cutting edge along the bottom.

Automobile drive shafts became mounting arms and the universal joints were used as hinges. Bolts welded to them fasten to the front axle of the tractor. The blade, which is center-mounted on a cross-piece made of pipe, pivots on the yoke of a universal joint. It's fastened with a kingpin. The blade is raised and lowered with cable running over pulleys.

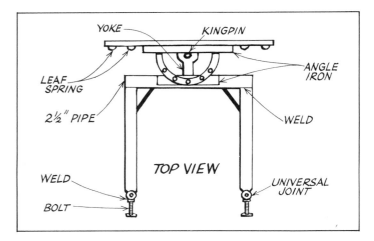

■ This device allows complete coverage when fertilizing pastures, even when you can't see your tire tracks well enough to use them as a guide. The marker is built from scrap angle iron and an old disk hiller. Mounted on the back of the fertilizer distributor, it swings up out of the way for pulling on the road.

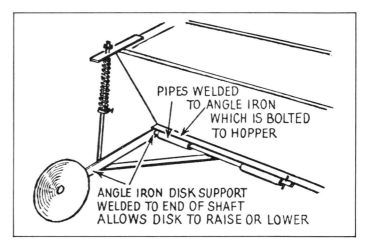

■ Usefulness of three-point hitch scraper blade can be increased by adapting it for forward and backward use. One simple way to do this is to weld an extra blade back to back with the original blade.

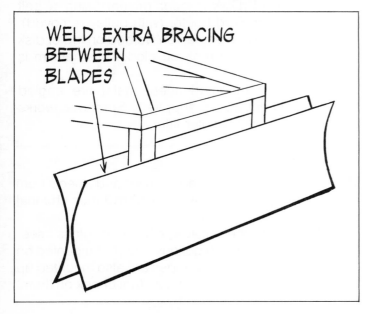

WELD EXTRA BRACING BETWEEN BLADES

■ This rear-mounted blade was built to stand up under rough use with a 140-horsepower tractor. Cut an old 10-foot grader blade out from under a road patrol and weld a 3½-inch shaft to the back in the center so it can be turned to the desired angle. Add a turntable and a frame out of double-strength pipe. It's rugged enough to do almost any job you want it for.

■ To push snow out of the way without buying any new equipment, the front of this tractor was rigged to take the scraper blade normally mounted on the three-point hitch at the rear.

First a heavy metal plate was fastened to the front of the tractor with eight bolts. Welded at right angles on the end of this plate are two "ears" bored to fit hitching points of the blade. A T-shaped bar is welded at center of plate. This bar has a slot at the top end for fastening a chain coming from the third hitch point of the blade. By means of this chain, the blade can be set at any height. Chain lets blade ride up over humps, then fall back to original position.

■ To control rate of flow on your fertilizer spreader from tractor seat, replace control lever with a hydraulic cylinder. Cylinder can be adjusted to put out fertilizer at any rate.

Time needed to rig up a two-way cylinder is about 15 minutes. Be sure to remove gauge plate on tongue to keep cylinder from bending the lever.

■ Increasing size of small, round hoppers on fertilizer distributors cuts down on number of stops for refilling. Here, discarded 10-gallon milk cans are used. Cut the bottom off each can. Then remove handles and cut off neck just below the lip at top. After flaring top of hopper, turn can upside down, put small end in hopper so it rests on flared top, and fasten it with stove bolts.

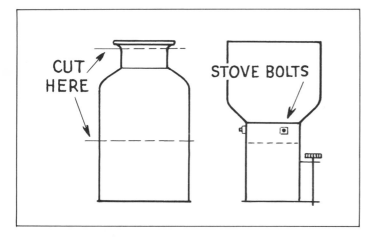

■ Drum filled with concrete holds rear end of tractor down and gives extra traction when heavy manure is handled with a front-end loader. It adds about 600 pounds more weight than is possible with wheel weights alone. Hitch to fit tractor is made from 1-inch rod that goes through 30-gallon drum.

■ Manure spreader, built on old 2-ton truck frame and mounted on truck's front axle, uses 6-inch auger to feed material onto spinning disc that scatters manure on field. Disk is gear driven, using a belt pulley drive from Ford tractor (with pulley removed). Two pieces of 1-inch angle iron welded on top of disk at right angles help break up clods. Mechanism is driven by p.t.o.

Sides of box made of sheet metal are angled sharply to keep auger supplied. Spreader works especially well with broiler litter.

■ This spray rig is mounted on axles and wheels from an old combine. Chassis is made from 3-inch channel iron.

Graduated on the outside, each fiber glass "see-through" tank holds 200 gallons. Boom is mounted on front of tractor. Pressure gauges are also mounted up front so operator can keep a constant check on them.

■ Put a gooseneck from drain hose of clothes washing machine on end of hose used to fill barrels or tanks of spray rigs. Gooseneck anchors hose over edge of container and there's no need to hold hose while you're filling tank.

■ Spray shield prevents herbicide drift. It rests on a steel runner fastened to the tow bar by a spring, allowing it to rise when it hits rocks, clumps, or roots. It's built of strap iron and lightweight sheet metal. Adjustable nozzles on underside of shield direct herbicide to sides and center of the rows.

 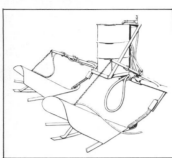

■ A four-row spray boom on the front of a tractor is good for spot-spraying perennial grasses in a hurry. Each row has three nozzles and a separate "flip" switch for easy spot-spraying. Boom is raised or lowered with a hydraulic cylinder.

■ Universal joints from a discarded combine drive shaft make hinges for folding boom on spray rig. Locking pins (sketched) keep boom rigid when in use. By pulling pin on each side, boom folds up, back, or forward for transporting.

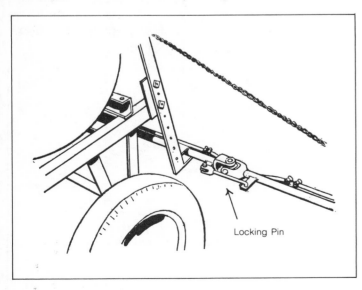

Locking Pin

■ To clean pipes and hoses in an orchard sprayer, use various-sized brushes sold for cleaning shotguns.

■ For quick and easy extra weight on the rear end of a tractor when using a front-end loader or front blade, attach two 55-gallon drums of water to a rack made to fit a three-point hitch.

Modifications & Conversions

■ Leveling board attached to disk pivots on two ½-inch bolts. When not needed, it swings up and lies out of the way on top of the disk. It is made of angle iron with strap iron braces.

■ To keep down plow and foot losses on cultivators, attach a small chain to the foot, wrap the other end around the cultivator beam, and fasten it with a slip-pin. This assures that you will still have the foot even though a bolt may loosen.

■ Sections of railroad track and heavy angle iron were used in this conversion of a wheeled chisel plow for three-point hitch mounting.

■ Concrete building blocks are good weights on a disk harrow. Sections of iron rail, stones, or logs often come loose while working in the field. A ½- x 11-inch bolt holds each block in place on the frame of the harrow. The block is held between old boards, each the same size as the side of the block. One board is under the frame, and the other is on top of the block. When mounted this way, the weights are easy to remove when not needed.

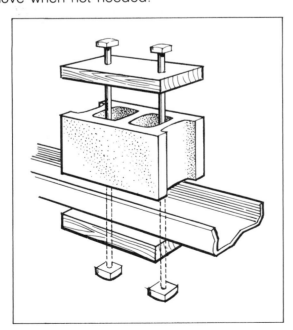

■ This field chopper is rigged so the delivery spout automatically stays pointed toward trailing wagon—even on sharp turns. Because of this, the tractor driver no longer has to worry about controlling delivery spout to keep chopped forage from being spilled outside wagon.

Instead, position of delivery spout is controlled by an iron rod bolted to it and extending to U-shaped guide on wagon. No matter which way harvester turns, this guide holds end of rod in same place so delivery spout always points to wagon box.

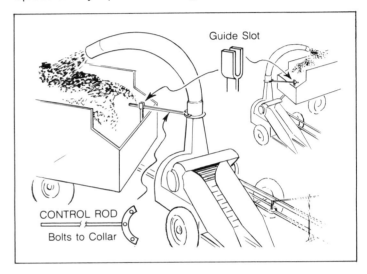

■ Grass boards on cutter bar of mower last longer and cause fewer stops for repairs when made of ¾-inch rubber belting instead of wood. Discarded belting came from conveyor belts used for handling sand, gravel, and limestone. Many conveyor systems in factories also use belting of this kind.

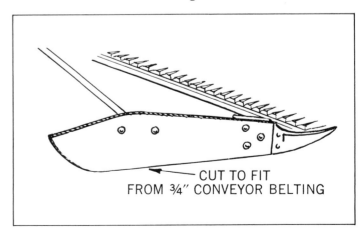

CUT TO FIT FROM ¾" CONVEYOR BELTING

■ Brackets, or storage hooks, hold tie-down ropes between loads on this hay hauling truck. These brackets are made of scrap metal and attached to under side of truck body. They are in line with rings on opposite side of truck to which ropes are tied when passed over top of load. This saves much time in looking for ropes and makes sure they are the proper length each time.

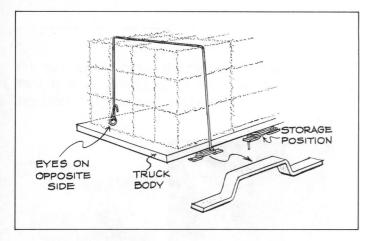

■ This mower blade was "half-soled" by making 4-inch lifts from heavy car springs for inner and outer shoes. Lifts keep mower blade from bouncing against the ground and picking up rocks that break sections and guards when clipping pasture weeds. The half-soles are welded to the bottom of the original sole.

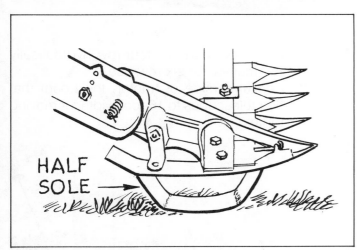

■ Even with mud scrapers in place, the space between the two outside disks on a tandem disk will often clog up, reducing effectiveness.

Here's one way to add to the efficiency of mud scrapers. Install a chain between each pair of outside disks on tandem disk.

This prevents mud and stalks from accumulating and clogging the space between disks.

■ An extra starter button mounted in the cab of this combine can unclog the header or cylinder in seconds. Just throw the combine out of gear, push the extra starter button, and roll the mechanism backward until it is unclogged. It surely beats getting down out of the cab and pulling the belt backward by hand.

The extra starter and its flywheel are mounted on the back of the header unit. A series of sprockets and chains give the starter additional power.

■ This pecan dehuller and cleaner knocks pecans out of the pods with beaters made from sections of an old rubber tire, then removes the trash by shaking.

The dehuller part works on an auger principle, with beaters on a shaft that extends through a piece of 10-inch tubing. There's about ¾-inch clearance between tubing and beaters, which are set at a slight angle so as to move pecans and trash through the tubing and feed it into the cleaner section.

An offset crank at the end of the main shaft gives a shaking motion to the cleaner section. This is a 4-foot x 8-inch sieve made up of rods spaced ¼-inch apart and hung on rocker arms.

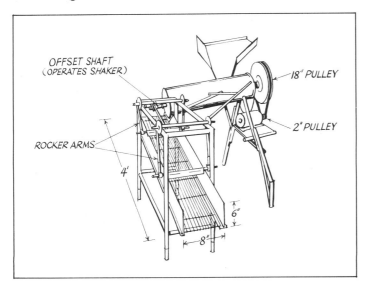

■ Gooseneck hitch on homebuilt land smoother makes it easy to use. The drag itself is made of 10-foot lengths of 2 x 6 timbers and quarter-inch metal strips from the scrap pile. Widths vary from 2 inches to 4 inches.

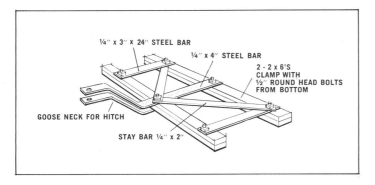

■ When mower knives (sickles) break near the knife head, move the knife head up the knife and add a short piece from an old knife. There's less strain at the far end of the knife, so the weld holds better than if it were near the knife head. Make the weld in the middle of a knife section for greater strength. First rivet the section in place, then grind the bar out in a V shape and weld.

■ Pepper pickers ride almost at ground level on this harvest aid. Conveyors lift peppers up and then toward front of tractor where they are dropped into container.

■ Telescoping boom adapts four-row hydraulically operated row marker for six-row use.

Mounted on underside of tractor, the boom that carries marker telescopes to 16-foot width for moving from field to field.

■ To do away with the need for taking chains off the drill when you change fields, weld hooks on back of the drill. When you are ready to move to another field, just hang chains over these hooks.

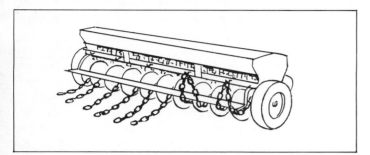

■ Scraper blade of 1 x 6 pine board solves problem of dirt sticking to wide press wheels used for smoothing soil for pre-emergence application of chemicals.

First weld a strip of flat iron on each side of press wheel so that arms supporting axle extend 2 inches past back edge of roller. At end of each extension weld a 4-inch upright. Small rods welded to each end of strap iron on which scraper blade is mounted fit into holes in the upright, so that blade swings between uprights. Board is held against roller with a medium-strength spring attached to bracket that holds nozzle.

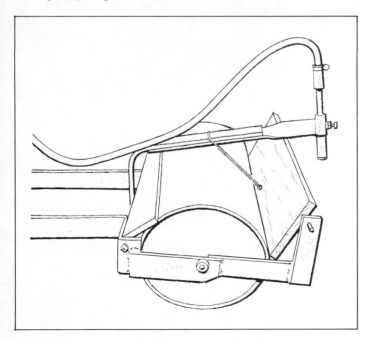

■ Conveyor chains and bars from an old manure spreader were used to build this baled hay elevator. Old mower sections riveted in the center of every other bar keep bales from slipping.

■ A signal to alert driver when twine tension is lost on haybaler saves the trouble of untied bales and the time needed to rethread the twine. The signal is an auto horn. It is activated by a toggle switch operated by tension arms on the twine cams. When tension arms on the twine cams relax, they close the circuit to auto horn by operating the switch.

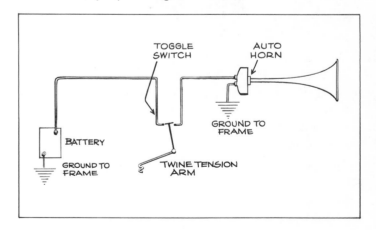

■ A push-button switch wired to the rear of the truck bed can sound the horn and signal the driver to stop during a hay-loading operation.

Service Tips

■ Taking off nuts is fast and easy when they have handles. These are welded rods bent at right angles. They're especially handy on nuts that have to be taken off quite often, such as those on bolts which hold tractor drawbar in place. In most cases, they can be taken off without bothering to use a wrench. Measure handle length before welding to make sure there is room enough for them to turn all the way around.

■ A dull knife on a hay baler can be sharpened in about 10 minutes, without removing it from the baler. Use a quarter-inch electric drill and a disc-type sanding attachment.

■ For a measuring cup that's always handy when adding a wetting agent, solder a soft drink can to the underside of your cottonpicker water tank lid.

■ Recording the purchase of farm equipment and appliances in a card file saves time when repairs are needed. List brand, model, cost, serial number, dealer's address and phone number, guarantee lengths and where it can be repaired on a single card. It's easy and saves time when repairs are needed.

■ Permanent instructions for lubrication painted on machinery ensure better maintenance. Also, by painting oil and water capacities on the side of the hood, you can save yourself a lot of running to the instruction manual. This is an especially good idea when several machines and several operators are involved.

■ Hoses at the "wash rack" where machinery is cleaned up are wrapped around 5-gallon cans when not in use. Tops of cans are removable so brushes and other cleaning supplies can be stored in them.

■ Place a square of tin under bedder bottom points when storing them on ground outside. This keeps points from sinking into dirt and prevents excess rust on points and bolts. Idea works for planters, too.

Hoists & Winches

■ This three-point tractor-mounted hoist is welded mostly from junked plow iron. Note the reinforcing brace rod welded to the top of the beam. Loops of iron rod at end of beam keep the log chain from dragging.

■ Worm gear from old binder or other piece of machinery is main working part of this winch. Rope or cable is wound on windless made of hardwood. Upright supports are 2 x 4's about 9 feet long spread about 4 feet apart at the bottom. Winch can be used on the ground or mounted on wagon, pickup, or tractor.

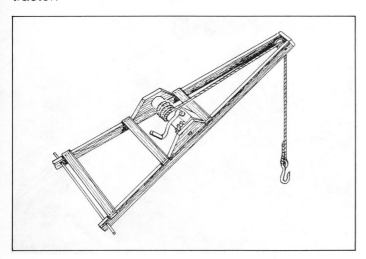

■ Portable hand winch is made from transmission of car or truck, a small drum with cable and a crank. Bolted to a sturdy wood base, it can be mounted on truck bed or other solid support and used to pull small tree stumps, fence posts, and heavy rocks, or to haul hay up into barn loft. Low gear is used for heavy loads; high gear for light loads.

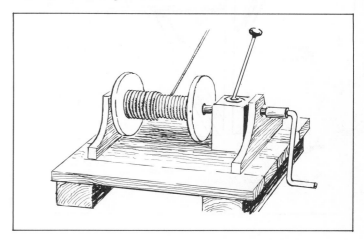

■ Hoist on this pickup bed adds to usefulness of the vehicle. The 4-foot-long upright pipe of the hoist fits snugly inside a base made from heavier pipe and welded to corner of pickup. The sliding collar at the bottom of the hinged angle brace can be raised and pinned in place just underneath the winch, thus raising the end of the arm almost 2 feet.

The winch is a heavy-duty boat trailer winch with ½-inch nylon rope and a snaphook. When not in use, the hoist is kept in place by tension on the rope snapped to an eyebolt.

■ This tractor boom was made in a farm shop. It's strong enough to handle anything the lift system on a 40-horsepower tractor can pick up.

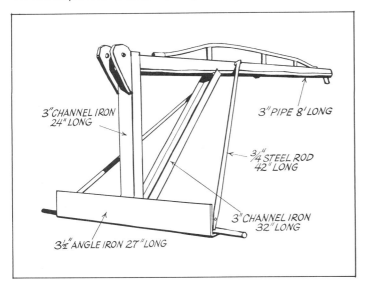

■ A boom and hoist that mounts on the tractor's three-point hitch is handy for mounting machinery as well as for lifting. It is lightweight but well reinforced by overhead bridging, and is easily and quickly attached to the tractor.

Trucks, Trailers, & Transports

■ Locked toolboxes on front of truck are mounted on 2-inch gaspipe welded to the bumper. They do not interfere with vision or night driving.

■ This dumpcart is built from the rear carriage of a discarded automobile. To repair or build fences, simply load the cart with posts, wire, and tools and go where the work is to be done. The dumpcart is just the right height from which to drive posts.

It can also be used to haul bales of hay, cans of water, and stones from the field. The cart cost only a few dollars because it was made from odds and ends found around the farm shop.

■ These carrier racks, made to transport aluminum irrigation pipe, can be swung out of the way or quickly removed from pickup truck when not in use.

Racks fit in brackets permanently attached to front and rear bumpers. Brackets are made by welding a short length of 2-inch pipe at right angles to a piece of heavy strap iron that is fastened to bumpers. Small cleat welded to vertical part of rack drops into notch at top of short pipe on bracket to keep rack from swinging back and forth when it is in use. Rotating racks half a turn when not in use cuts width of truck to normal clearance.

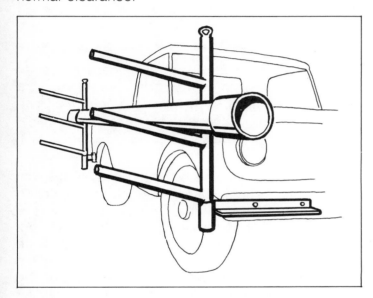

■ This handy ladder for climbing on truck beds was made of ¼-inch deck plate and ¾-inch black pipe. Steps are 8½ inches wide, 18 inches long, and 11½ inches apart. Pieces of pipe that fit over tire are 16 inches long. Other measurements are as shown in diagram.

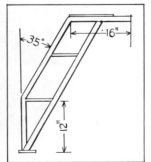

■ A bootjack cut into the back bumper of a pickup truck, just behind the right rear wheel, makes the switch from rubber boots to shoes quite easy. The tailgate can be let down for a seat when using the bootjack. Edges of the "V" the torch cuts into the bumper can be smoothed with a file to prevent cutting footwear.

■ To protect the bottom of aluminum boat while hauling it in a truck, make a wooden frame of 2 x 2's to place in the truck bed. Three of the 2 x 2's are 9 feet long and two are 29 inches long. For bracing, use two pieces of plywood, each 8 x 29 inches across the center. The boat slides on six discarded rollers from a wringer-type clothes washer. Place rollers in pairs at front, center, and back of framework. They turn in bushings made from ½-inch pipe. These sit in notches cut in the framework and are held down by a small metal strip over the top. Boat is held in place with two long leather straps.

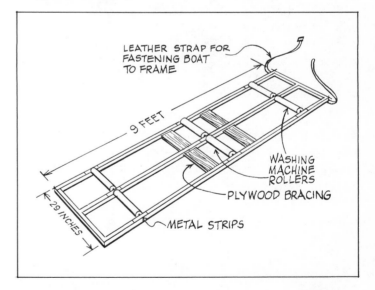

■ To warn when truck or car fenders get too close to machinery or fences, weld a 5-foot upright of pipe on each end of the front bumper. Paint these guides white so you can see them at night when the headlights are on.

■ Coil springs from a junked automobile make good overload springs for a farm trailer. They are placed between lower frame and bolster and held in place by welding at the bottom. Pipe is welded to bolster to keep spring in position at top.

For best results, use matched springs. Check them first to see that they are close to the same height by setting them side by side.

■ A hydraulically operated trailer hoists and hauls disk harrow. Rotating the U-shaped axle raises and lowers wheels. Disk is fastened with chains welded in place. Extra brackets are for two smaller single-acting cylinders that can be used when this double-acting cylinder is in use on some other implement.

■ This trailer carries a 560-gallon tank big enough for refueling tractors in the field. Axles came from an old mobile home. Fenders came from a local manufacturer. The trailer carries its own spare tire on the rear and is wired for lights. Fuel is transferred with a 12-volt electric pump.

■ Unloading with a scoop is easier when you put a wide board in trailer or wagon box before loading. No need to have the board fastened down.

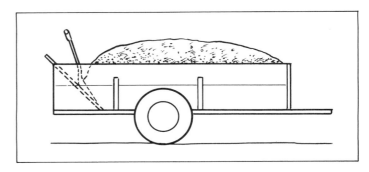

■ To keep from knocking grease caps off trailer wheels when going through woods, cover them with a strip of metal. Metal strips about 3 inches wide can easily be bolted on the wheels.

■ Installing a trapdoor in the bottom of a trailer saves time and money in unloading ear corn, grain, cotton seed, and other materials. Here are some advantages: There are no heavy endgates to lift out and put back in. One-third of the load slides out by itself. Since the opening is near the center of the trailer, there's a shorter distance for shoveling. You save considerable wear and tear on yourself and the trailer. The trailer can just be driven alongside the elevator without the job of backing.

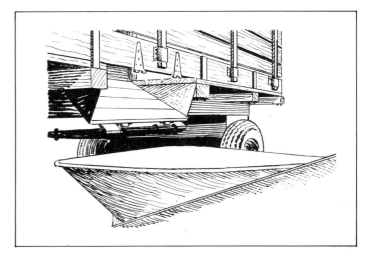

■ This two-way "pickup" trailer can be used on three-point hitch of tractor or can be pulled behind auto.

With tongue in place, this small trailer is suitable for trips to town and general highway use. Tongue can be taken off just by removing one pin. Then trailer can be mounted on three-point hitch and used in row crops where turning at ends is a problem. It's especially handy for harvesting truck crops, hauling fertilizer, or picking up roots in new land.

Plywood box is 6 feet long. It's built on welded steel frame of ¼- x 2- x 2-inch angle.

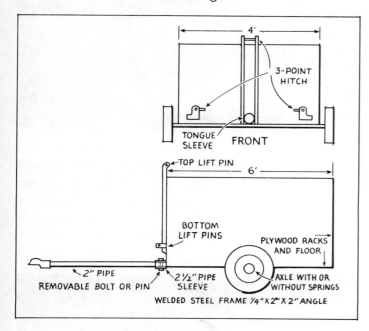

■ Tie plates bolted to sides of the trailer floor make machinery hauling safer and easier. The plate of this one is ¼ x 2 ½ x 7 inches. The loop of ⅝-inch rod is 3½ inches high. It is welded to one side of the plate, and leans in.

■ This "headache rack" serves as a roll bar and protects the rear window from breakage without obstructing the view. Besides, it's good advertising.

Outside framework is 1½-inch pipe. Piece across the bottom is 1-inch angle iron. Letters are made from ½-inch metal rods. They're mounted on part of old rake wheel.

■ Wide surplus belting is a valuable addition to the metal floor of a pickup bed because (1) it provides a firm footing for people and for livestock; (2) it protects the paint on the floor and holds down rust; (3) it will prevent some dents by absorbing the shock of falling firewood pieces, rock, scrap, and other items being loaded.

■ This implement carrier lets one man load and transport without unhitching the implement. It is chained to the drawbar, and therefore best for short hauls at slow speeds.

Running gear is from the front end of a car. Floor is about 6 feet long and extends past the wheels so the weight of the harrow on the back end will overbalance and raise the front end. Floor is built several inches higher than wheels so wide implements can stick out over edges. Back trailer against a post, rock, or ditch to load and unload.

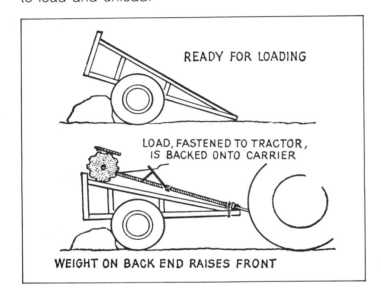

■ Wheel guards on both sides of rear wheels keep truck cleaner and also keep rocks from flying.

■ An economical grain truck can be made from an old milk truck.

Pull the sheet metal top off the box and stretch two chains across the middle to strengthen the sides.

■ Open box on three-point hitch serves many purposes. It can be raised close to wagon height or lowered to rest on the ground. Box is 3 feet high. Base is 3 x 6 feet. Angle iron welded to steel frame under the box is drilled to fit pin for pulling lightweight trailer.

■ This lightweight platform mounts on the three-point hitch of a small tractor. The frame is built of angle iron and scrap metal from a plow frame. The floor is of cypress. Carrier is handy for hauling small loads which otherwise would take a truck or wagon, and for fence building.

■ A utility light for pickup truck can be made by mounting a light on a C-clamp. Drill a hole in the clamp large enough to take the mounting bolt of the light bracket. A ground wire fastens under the lamp rim and is held with one of the rim screws. Because the light has its own ground, it can be clamped anywhere it's needed. The clamp also makes a good base for setting it on the ground when fixing flat tires.

■ Here's an easy way to add steps to the inside of a cotton trailer to make climbing out easier. Form C-shaped steps from ½-inch sucker rod, and weld them to uprights at rear of trailer, as shown in the sketch. The same idea can be adapted to a wooden trailer by using rod with threaded ends or welding bolts to the ends, and also welding a large washer as a stop on each end.

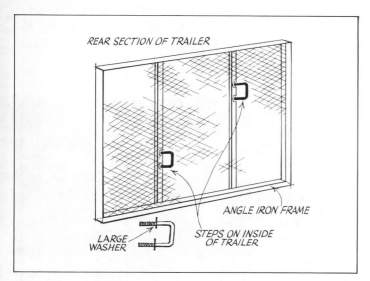

REAR SECTION OF TRAILER

ANGLE IRON FRAME

STEPS ON INSIDE OF TRAILER

LARGE WASHER

■ Hogs, feed, fencing, and other materials can be loaded easily on this carrier that attaches to the tractor's two-point fast-hitch system. The 5- x 7-foot carrier is framed with welded pipe and has a 2-inch plank floor. Sides of the carrier are 41 inches high and covered with hog-panel fencing. A pair of 3-inch channel irons, not visible in the photograph, supports the floor. Heavy plywood doors, each 2 feet wide, slide up and down in angle iron guides. Rear panel can be taken out by pulling rods at each end or swung open from either side by leaving one of the rods in place.

■ Frame for this hefty carrier is made of heavy angle iron. When fitted with stakes, it can be used for hauling fenceposts. It can also be floored with rough-sawn lumber or fitted with a crate for taking sows and pigs to pasture. Hitch welded to crosspiece is convenient for pulling small trailer or sled and for moving hog lot equipment.

■ Removable pipe standard that slips into larger diameter pipe sockets welded to angle iron frame makes this three-point hitch carrier ideal for hauling fenceposts.

Hitches

■ Here's one way to fix wagon tongue of pipe so it can be made longer when wagon is to be pulled behind baler or corn picker. Cut tongue in two and thread both ends. Put pipe coupling on both ends so extra length of pipe can be put in place when needed.

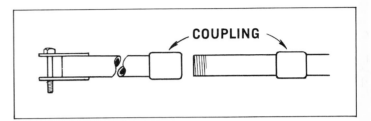

■ To make a telescoping tongue, slip smaller diameter pipe inside tongue after it is cut in two. Drill holes where needed for bolts to go through both sizes of pipe to make tongue as long as you want it.

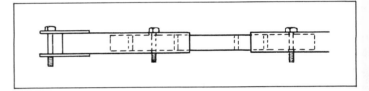

■ Sliding drawbar on tractor allows leeway for coupling grain wagons and machinery without help or a second try. Hitch pin (arrow) is fitted with a ring for safety and drops in place as tractor is backed to shorten sliding drawbar. Drawbar (bottom arrow) locks in place for towing.

■ This electrical circuit tester can be made in about 15 minutes from a regular flashlight. The flashlight can still be used in the usual way.

First, solder one strand of lampcord wire ahead of the switch. This wire comes through a hole drilled in the bottom of the case.

Then, solder a ground wire to the case. To test fuses, hold wires on either end, as shown. If light burns, the fuse is good. Extension cords, switches, bulbs, and many other things are tested the same way. If the thing being tested is good, it will complete the circuit, and the light will burn. Remember that this is to test fuses and other things that have been removed from the circuit. Do not attempt to test a hot circuit, as this will burn out the flashlight bulb.

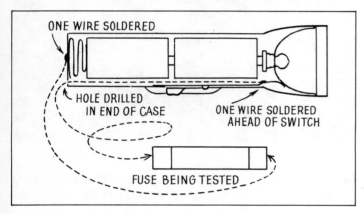

ONE WIRE SOLDERED

HOLE DRILLED IN END OF CASE

ONE WIRE SOLDERED AHEAD OF SWITCH

FUSE BEING TESTED

■ Change tires quickly with this wheel holder that lets you use a tire-removing tool just like those used in tire repair shops. Holder is made from an old car axle with 6 inches cut off the flange. Remove all bolts, drive one back in from the opposite side of the flange, then bolt unit in place with the flange down. With wheel on holder, you can slip tire-removing tool under bead and pull it around axle to remove tire.

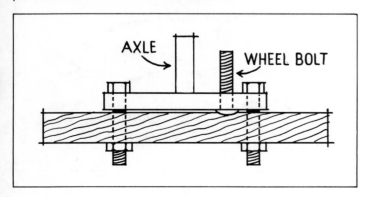

AXLE

WHEEL BOLT

■ This portable power source is handy inside or outside the shop. Drills or other equipment can be plugged into one outlet and a trouble light into the other. An old disk is used for the base. The ring on top of the iron pipe upright makes it easy to move. Cord is wound around two hooks.

■ A cotton picker spindle makes a good "ease out" if the pipe breaks off your grease gun and you cannot get a grip on the pipe from the outside.

Burs on the spindle will dig into soft metal, making the spindle a satisfactory tool for emergency use.

■ This lighting stand gets light where it's needed for night repair work. It's adjustable and tall enough to light properly without blinding.

Also, the outlet at the base is good for plugging in an extension cord for another light or small power tools.

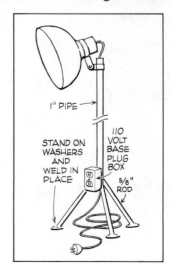

1" PIPE

110 VOLT BASE PLUG BOX

STAND ON WASHERS AND WELD IN PLACE

5/8" ROD

■ Here's a useful pipe vise and machinists' vise table. A 32-inch square of quarter-inch steel plate is welded to a 50-gallon oil barrel that is filled with sand. To make the job easier, complete welding before filling with sand. Matching slots, about 2 x 12 inches in the plate and 6 x 16 inches in the barrel, were cut so the barrel could be easily filled. Vises are placed at opposite corners of the table. Other corners are rounded. For heavy work, you can weld braces from corner to the barrel.

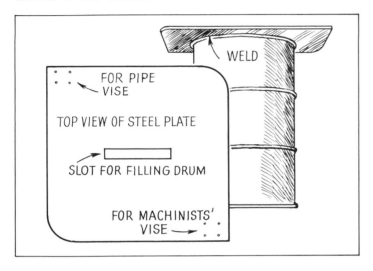

■ This movable shop anvil was made from a section of large-sized I-beam (bought at a junkyard) welded to the top of a well casing pipe which is braced by three angle iron "feet."

■ A 250-pound flywheel off a junked haybaler forms the base of this sturdy anvil stand. Weld a 14-inch piece of 6-inch pipe to the center of the flywheel and a 12- x 14-inch piece of 1-inch plate to the top of the pipe. Anvil is tack welded to this plate. This combination stands a comfortable 31 inches high and is heavy enough not to move under heavy use.

■ Key puller gets at those long, square keys used to keep shafts from turning in hubs or pulleys on machinery.

This puller is a long shaft with a flat plate welded at one end. The shaft moves inside a short length of pipe or metal sleeve which is used as a hammer against the end plate. In use, end of the shaft is spot welded to the key. Then the sliding sleeve is banged against end plate to pull key out of its slot. Key puller is ready to use again after key and shaft are sawed apart with a hacksaw.

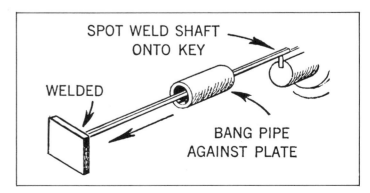

■ Old valve stem from truck tube is basic part of this tool that makes air-blast cleaning easier. Designed for hand-holding against air chuck, it is handy for hard-to-reach places or small parts.

To make, solder 10-inch length of ⅛-inch copper tubing to end of valve stem. Turn flange around, and lock in place with two nuts.

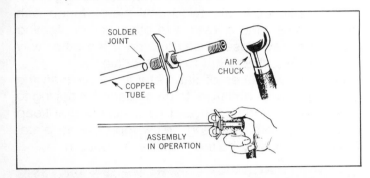

■ This portable, hydraulic press is built around a hydraulic truck jack welded in place. Adjustable table can be held in four different positions by pins that fit through holes drilled in uprights. Frame of the press is made of 4- x 2- x ¼-inch channel iron. Spring tension returns jack to normal position when valve is opened.

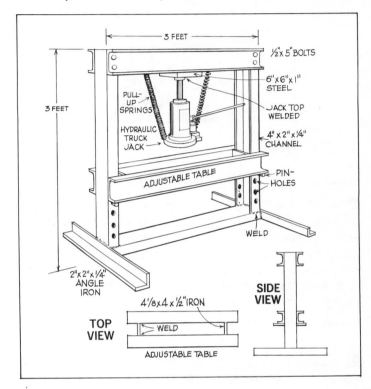

■ An air compressor is handy around the farm and in the shop. Mounting it on a two-wheeled cart will increase its usefulness. You can use car wheels and a shortened axle under a frame welded from channel iron, pipe, and strap iron.

■ Here's one way to carry a small vise on the back end of a pickup truck. Weld two short lengths of angle iron together so they will slip down into the pockets on the back end of the pickup—the pockets where the cattle sides go. Then mount the vise on this. It can be put on or taken off easily. In an emergency, it can even be used as a wrench.

■ Scrap pipe and heavy expanded metal form this handy step stool for the farm shop. The expanded metal forms a slip-resistant surface for the mechanic working on truck or tractor.

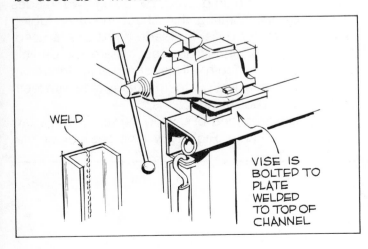

■ For an inexpensive tire pump, use a one-cylinder gasoline engine belt-driven by an electric motor. Both motors were salvaged from discarded lawn mowers. Ordinary spark plug tire pump is screwed into the spark plug hole of the engine. Blade on the electric mower is replaced with a pulley.

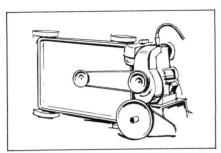

■ A battery charger can be made by attaching a 12-volt automobile generator to a ¼-horsepower electric motor by means of a V-belt. Voltage regulator and ammeter are wired the same as if used on the car. For added convenience, add an adjustable voltage regulator that can be varied from 5 to 35 amps by using a screwdriver.

■ Battery charger mounted on rubber-tired wheels is easy to move over rough ground. Frame built of 1-inch-square tubing protects charger when it is left standing in traffic areas after the vehicle is started.

■ To get a better grip on a screwdriver, slip a piece of rubber hose over the handle. This also makes the screwdriver shockproof.

■ Quick-action vise is designed for sharpening chain saws. Basic parts are two metal plates faced with heavy leather and a lever with offset roller. Flipping lever one way closes vise; flipping it the other way opens vise just enough to move chain.

One of the pieces of flat metal is larger than the other—just enough larger to give space for bolting to sawhorse or workbench and for brackets that keep small plate from dropping below top of large plate. Plates are loosely bolted together at bottom.

■ Hacksaws used in small shops and around home ordinarily can be improved by using two blades instead of one. Cutting thin sheet metal or tubing quickly breaks or dulls the blade if just one is used. However, if two blades are used, there will be little breakage and the teeth will stay sharp much longer. In using two blades, just put them side by side with teeth pointing in opposite directions.

If you do a great deal of sawing, be sure to get a saw with a heavy frame. Rigidity will increase blade life.

■ When emery wheels get grooved or rounded and no wheel dresser is at hand, you can do the job with an old emery wheel. With a little care, you can do a good job of truing even with just a piece of an old emery wheel.

■ Base of this blacksmith's forge is a steel automobile wheel on 36-inch legs of ½-inch pipe. Center of wheel—the fire pit—is closed by welding in a piece of flat scrap iron which has small holes in it to let air through.

Compressed air that fans flame comes through 2-inch pipe welded across bottom of the wheel. Fitting for air hose is welded on one end. Other end is capped or plugged in use, but opened for blowing out ashes. Short length of pipe welded in center of this pipe directs arm upward to fire. Regulate air flow with outlet valve on compressor.

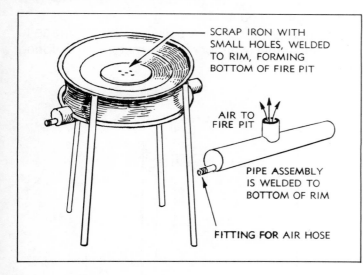

SCRAP IRON WITH SMALL HOLES, WELDED TO RIM, FORMING BOTTOM OF FIRE PIT

AIR TO FIRE PIT

PIPE ASSEMBLY IS WELDED TO BOTTOM OF RIM

FITTING FOR AIR HOSE

■ Base made from screen of old hammermill makes it easier to mount small electric motor for different uses. There are enough mounting holes in a base of this kind so belt can be tightened easily and so motor can be fitted to many uses. Use quarter-inch screen and weld it to the motor. Drill the holes larger when needed.

■ This small pressure washer is mounted on an old lawnmower chassis, so it can be rolled in and out of the shop easily. The hose can be wrapped around the mower handle when not in use.

■ Funnel that won't rust can be made quickly from empty plastic bottle such as is used for household bleach or detergent. Just cut off bottom with sharp knife or scissors. Part not used for funnel is handy for holding nails or bolts.

■ Making the bench grinder movable allows it to be taken outside the farm shop when machinery is to be repaired, and saves steps in the shop, too. Base is of deck plate fitted with casters. Center post is a length of well casing. On top is welded a small plate to which grinder is bolted.

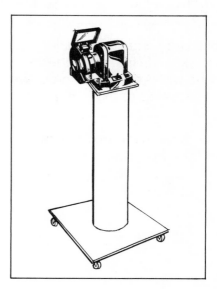

■ Vise to hold circle saws and hand saws for sharpening is made from two 4-foot pieces of 2- x 6-inch lumber. Hinged part is 18 inches long. Hole for ½- by 5-inch bolt is drilled after the two parts connected with hinge have been nailed in place. Short crank is welded to nut for quick fastening.

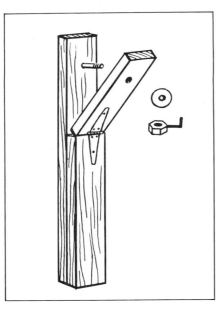

■ If you want an electric hacksaw and can't afford one, build your own, with some old scrap iron and an old washing machine motor, using one V-belt pulley and two V-belts.

Using a connecting rod from an old truck motor, you can build a crankshaft to push and pull the blade.

■ When building portable hydraulic press, make the jack unit so it will slide from one side to the other. This way it can be more easily centered over the work. Springs are fastened to the jack plate.

■ Old vacuum cleaner is good for supplying airblast for forge in farm blacksmith shop.

Drills

■ A removable handle on electric drill is a handy container for small drills. To make, replace original handle with a ¾-inch pipe nipple and cap.

■ This drill press is built with parts from an old haybaler. Base is an old auto tire and wheel, with a hollow drive shaft welded to it. Fitted loosely inside is a 1-inch rod that is also welded to the base. This rod extends 1 foot beyond the top of the hollow shaft. It is braced at the top with an L-shaped piece of iron welded to the outside of the drive shaft.

Drill slides up and down on a length of pipe that fits over this rod and also inside the drive shaft.

Chuck is threaded on shaft that has pulley on other end and is bushed inside a short length of pipe. This and motor are mounted on 18-inch metal bar welded to the sliding mount.

For raising drill, mount a pulley on the top brace to guide cable that is attached near motor and to spring fastened at the base.

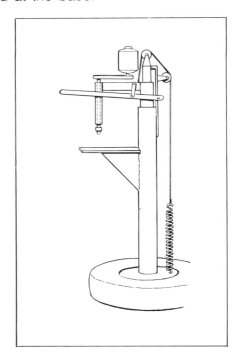

■ To make this bench-model drill press more usable, it was mounted upside down and the drill head was reversed. To do this, bolt the drill press to a sturdy bench, take off the table that holds work to be drilled, turn legs of bench up and bolt them to ceiling, then mount drill head in proper position.

If work to be drilled is on a table equipped with casters, it can be rolled into position under the drill. This is especially handy for heavy or unwieldy objects. Keep removable table of drill press handy so it can be put back on when desired.

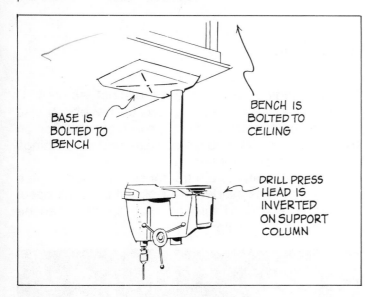

■ To keep from breaking small drills, use a bushing made from a short length of wood dowel or other scrap of wood. Leave just enough of the drill sticking through to go through the material you are drilling.

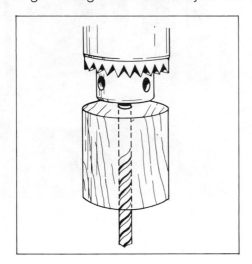

■ For help in drilling true vertical or horizontal holes, tape a spirit level to your drill.

■ Home-custom-built drill press is powered with motor from an old spin-dry washer. Chuck is fastened to shaft extension of gear head. Slow speed of the two-speed gear head is just right for drilling large holes. Fast speed is fine for small drills or soft material.

Framework of drill press is of 1-inch pipe.

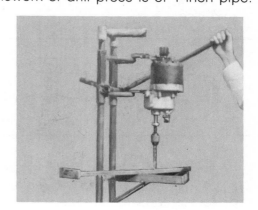

Nuts & Bolts

■ Broken studs that are hard to get at can be removed quite easily if you have use of a welding outfit. First thing you need is a short piece of pipe that will fit loosely into the opening, as indicated in sketch. Use welding outfit to fill pipe with enough molten metal to weld it firmly to the stud. (Pipe keeps metal away from threads.) Stud can then be removed with a pipe wrench.

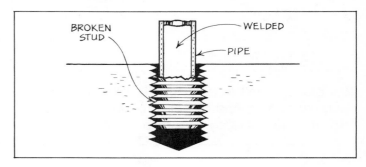

■ Lighter fluid can be used instead of penetrating oil to loosen rusty nuts and bolts.

■ Troublesome bolt threads that refuse to catch can be cured this easy way: Saw slits in end of bolt—at right angles to each other as shown in sketch. Then with soft hammer reduce diameter of end of bolt.

Another idea is to split the bolt in the same fashion, then split nut in two, place it over the split end, and squeeze in a vise.

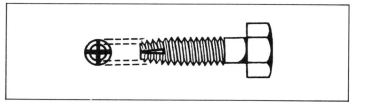

■ Paint exposed threads of bolts with red lead metal primer to protect threads from rust and corrosion. The paint will also keep nuts from vibrating loose, but permit removal with a wrench.

■ To hold threaded rods or bolts firmly in a vise without damaging the threads, cut through one side of a square nut or one angle of a hexagon nut with a hacksaw. Then thread nut onto rod or bolt, and clamp nut tightly in vise.

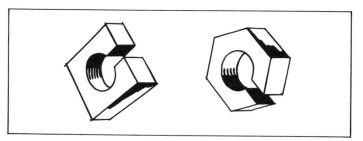

■ Vibration can't loosen nut fixed this way. Use a hacksaw to split end of bolt protruding above nut. Then spread it slightly with cold chisel.

■ Hurting a hand or arm when the wrench slips off a nut or the bolt breaks can be avoided. Carefully fit the wrench to the nut and then brace yourself so that the pull on the wrench will be about one-eighth of a circle at a time. This may seem slow, but it usually turns out to be a saving in time and temper.

Welding

■ This welding table has three distinct features: 1) wheels to make it easy to move to the job, 2) vise mounted on one corner, and 3) piece of angle iron on top to make it easier to weld shafts and other things that need to be kept lined up.

Work stool features old tractor seat welded to pipe upright that slips inside larger pipe that forms base. Pin fits holes drilled through pipe so stool can be adjusted to best height.

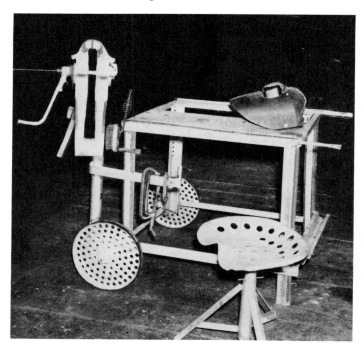

■ Welding cart made from old auto parts can be pulled easily, steers well, and is large enough to accommodate extra equipment.

■ A frame of scrap ¾-inch angle iron welded in the form of a rectangle just large enough to hold two firebricks will protect the top of your welding table. The bricks are easier to replace than the entire tabletop when they become worn from repeated heating by the oxyacetylene flame. The small unit can be moved out of the way when the full tabletop is needed.

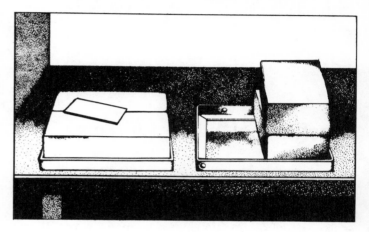

■ Junked refrigerators make good storage cabinets for welding rods. This one is fitted with partitions welded from strap iron and sheet metal. A 25-watt bulb rigged to burn inside all the time will keep the rods dry.

■ Welding rods of various kinds and lengths are easy to pick out from this rack at the end of the workbench.

Rack is made from short pieces of pipe welded side by side and then to a frame of angle iron. Spaces are left between lengths of pipe to show the various lengths and sizes of rods and are thus easier to remove.

■ Welding and cutting table can be made from a discarded oil drum. Either the 55- or the 30-gallon size is satisfactory. The top is cut out and replaced with a grill made from reinforcement rods spaced about 2 inches apart. Sparks and slag fall through. There's a 12- x 16-inch cleanout door at the bottom. Hooks on each side are for hanging torch and helmet.

Mechanical & Repair Tips

■ A heavy-duty, bright-colored plastic shopping bag makes a fine spread for laying out wrenches above heavy grass, grain stubble, flattened-down corn-stalks, or wherever you have to make a machinery adjustment in the field. It helps keep tools from getting lost. The bag is strong enough to carry quite a few tools back to the toolbox after you've made the adjustment.

■ An old leather belt is a big help in removing a screw-in type oil filter when you can't get a good grip on it with your hands and don't have a tool built especially for the job.

Just place the belt around the filter, run the loose end through the buckle, and tug on it.

■ Damaged insulation on battery cables is not necessarily a reason for buying new cable. Slipping ½-inch plastic hose over old cable is all that's needed to make it usable, providing worn insulation is the only thing wrong. Hose easily slips over end of cable that fastens to starter.

■ The plastic top from a 1-pound coffee can will make a cover top for a quart can of oil that has been opened. It keeps insects and trash out.

■ An outside toolbox can be made from a hog feeder that had rusted away at the bottom. Cut off the top part—about 24 inches down—and put in a pressure-treated wood bottom. Then paint it and set it on cement blocks.

■ To replace spark plug in hard-to-reach place, hold plug in a short length of rubber hose until you get it started. If you begin to cross-thread, the hose will turn free and prevent damage. Finish the job with a regular spark plug wrench.

■ To test anti-freeze, draw a small amount from the radiator into a tin can, cover with metal foil, and put it in the freezer. If this small amount does not freeze, it will "hold" the radiator down to zero.

■ A small washer soldered about ¼ inch from the end of oilcan spout is especially handy in tight places where spring-capped oilers can be reached with only one hand.

This washer lifts the spring cap and the oilcan spout is right where it belongs for filling the oil cup.

■ Rubber-tipped hammer for taking dents out of metal objects you don't want scarred can be made from regular carpenter's hammer. Just slip white crutch tip over hammer head.

■ Heating heavy metal without a forge can be done quite easily by using a shallow hole in the ground as a substitute for the fire-pot. To get air to the bottom of the fire, bury a short length of a 1¼-inch metal pipe in a small trench leading into the hole. The other end is above ground. To this, attach hose from "blower end" of vacuum cleaner.

■ A discarded milker inflation, with the cushion end cut off, makes an ideal flexible spout. It can easily be forced down over the metal spout of a 5-gallon oil can. A radiator hose clamp holds the inflation in place. This does away with need for a funnel.

■ Need light for chores and repair jobs away from the power lines? Here's an easy way to get it: Mount an electric outlet box on your truck and power it from the truck battery. A regulation extension cord and a 6-volt or 12-volt bulb, which looks like an ordinary light bulb, complete the setup. It may take a little searching to find bulbs, but they are available.

■ Battery jumper cables won't get tangled if you tape them together about every 12 inches.

■ Wrenches and small hand tools painted with orange paint are much easier to keep up with out of doors.

■ For an easy supply of distilled water (for batteries), save the ice and water from your refrigerator when you defrost it. Or collect water from an air conditioner. Just tap the drain line with plastic pipe or tubing and store water in a plastic bottle. Several gallons a day can be collected in hot, humid weather.

■ Here's how to keep your supply of lubricating oil clean when you need to use just a small amount out of the can from time to time. Punch two holes in top of can with large common nails. Pour out oil needed. Replace nails in top of can, using small leather washers under heads of nails.

■ When caught without the proper tool for installing rings in a small-bore engine, try a screw-type radiator hose clamp.

■ To prevent hard starting of tractors on wet or damp mornings, slip a fairly heavy plastic bag over each magneto or distributor and tape it in place. Make a small hole for each wire and push the wire through; then press the rubber caps on the wire down over the plastic bag. You can do the same thing for a pickup to eliminate easy "drowning out."

Shop Storage

■ Plastic jugs can be used as a catalog system for bolts and other small items by cutting a hole in the side and stringing them up on a wire or other support above the workbench.

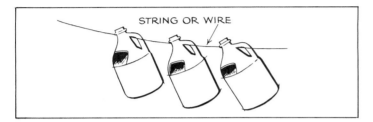

■ Five-gallon "pour-spout" cans, such as those oil comes in, can be altered to be more useful for a number of purposes. Cut out about one-third of top of can, opposite the spout. Make starting hole at edge with a chisel and then saw with a keyhole hacksaw. Do not cut all the way to center of top. Leave part of top with the lift handle. Smooth edges of cut with a file. Inside of can must be cleaned thoroughly and coated with aluminum paint.

Large opening makes can easy to fill from spigot or bucket or by dipping.

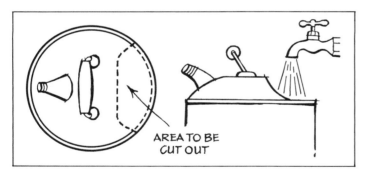

■ Keep chain saw blade in good condition by storing both blade and bar in a bath of motor oil. A cream can or old hand-sprayer can is a good container to use.

■ Squeeze-type plastic bottles with snip-off tops make good oilcans. Keep several of these in various places around the shop, so that they are always handy.

■ Set of bins for nuts, bolts, and other small parts is made from large tin cans. They are fastened together by soldering at front, back, and side.

■ Large safety pins, 4 inches or more in length, are handy for holding small articles such as washers, fishhooks, extra nuts, or small dies. Just string the items on a pin, then snap it shut, and hang on a nail. To save space, pins can be strung on wire or heavy cord.

■ Old leather belts make good tool holders. Tack the belts to the wall, leaving enough slack between tacked sections to form a holder for various tools, from claw hammer to tin snips.

■ Square-cornered anti-freeze and oilcans with one end removed form compartments on shelves of this storage unit. They can be removed from the back. LP-gas torch and spare cylinder fit in can fastened to side of cabinet. Entire unit is mounted on heavy duty casters.

■ Protect your circle saw with an old bicycle tire. Cut rim from one side of tire and slip it over saw blade to protect you and teeth when saw is not in use.

■ Use cardboard tubes to control your extension cords. A 35 mm. film carton or tubes from kitchen or bathroom tissue work well. Just fold the cord to the size desired and slip it through the tube.

■ Quarter-inch mesh hardware cloth can be used to hold a multitude of tools compactly and in an orderly fashion. The mesh is bent in the shape of a "U." It is sufficiently stiff so that one side may be hung from regular pegboard hangers. This allows screwdrivers, pliers, and other similar slim tools to be arranged with easy access to any one of them.

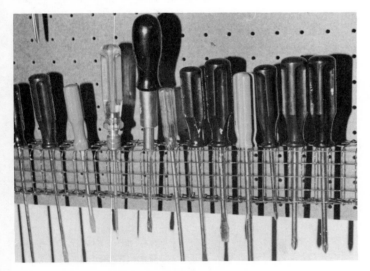

■ Old bread pans make ideal trays for storing small items. Mounted under the workbench as shown, they slide in and out easily.

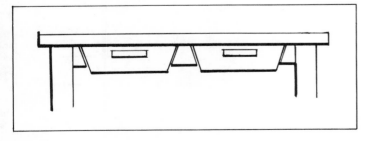

■ This nail bin has 32 plywood compartments and can be turned all the way around with one finger. Bin is hung on center shaft—4 feet of 2-inch pipe—that is welded in upright position onto spindle of wheel from front of old car.

Bolts or screws for fastening bin to center shaft go through small metal lugs welded to shaft. Wheel that forms base is mounted on four swivel rollers so bin can be moved easily.

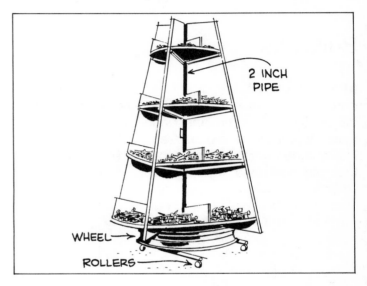

■ Several TV dinner containers tacked to workbench will hold small screws and parts when working on a repair job. There is just enough rim to keep parts from being knocked off the bench—and separate compartments for everything. Nailing them down keeps trays, parts, and all from being knocked off.

■ A carrying board such as this helps keep tangles and knots out of ropes and extension cords. Good size board to use is about 8 x 12 inches.

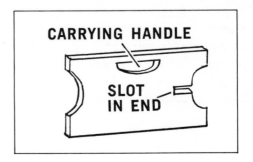

Chapter VI
CONSTRUCTION

Buildings

■ This welded scaffolding bracket holds planks securely. It was made of flat iron, 1½-inches wide. It can be quickly unhooked and changed by pulling two nails. Double-headed ones are used for speedy work. Nail notches were cut in at an angle so that weight of the load kept them tight against nails.

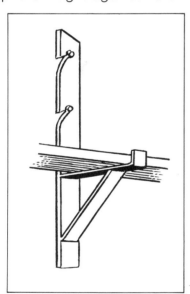

■ An old refrigerator door makes a good entrance for a storm shelter. Instead of re-mounting the door, just cut the back out of the refrigerator, then set it in place. Remove the latch and put springs on to keep the door shut.

■ Here's an anchor system that keeps a concrete floor from buckling even where excess ground water pressure is a problem. It holds the normal 4-inch-thick floor in place.

Idea of the system is to add weight of ground beneath floor to weight of floor and thus keep water from pushing floor up. Place anchor underground before pouring floor and tie it to reinforcing rods. Reinforcing rods should be near top surface of floor instead of near bottom. Correct depth for anchor is 2½ times distance floor is below ground level. Thus, if floor is 4 feet beneath ground level, anchor should be 10 feet below ground level (not 10 feet below floor level).

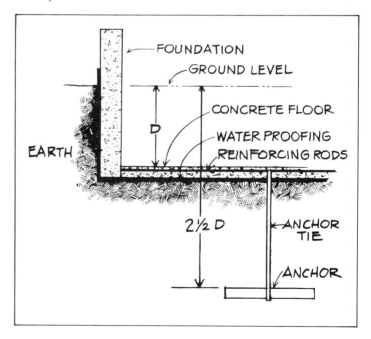

■ When making double doors for a barn or other building, try building a wide door in place; then sawing it in two. To do this, run battens across the opening full length, nailing them to temporary blocks on inside of the posts on which the doors will be hung.

With the top and bottom battens secured, go ahead and build the doors in the position they will hang. After bracing and hinging, saw battens in middle of opening and have two swinging doors already hung. Temporary blocks are then removed.

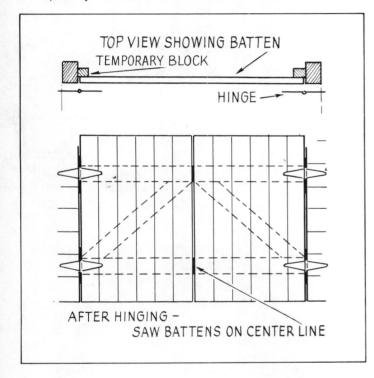

■ Carry nails in the cuff of your blue jeans when laying wood floors. Large safety pins keep cuff turned up to form a pocket.

■ Workmen planning to install ceiling tile can reduce chances of soiling tile by dusting their hands with ordinary cornstarch before handling. This shields tile from unsightly smudges.

■ This plastic-covered hotbed is inexpensive, easy to build, and suitable for use in your backyard. Better yet, you can move it when you want to. It's only 5 feet long x 3½ feet wide.

A 360-watt soil-heating cable, thermostatically controlled to shut off at 70° F., is used for heat. Two pieces of plastic film cover the frame. Overlapped at the top, they are held taut with snap clothespins. Welded wire mesh (8 gauge) is used for the frame. This is similar to the wire mesh used for reinforcing concrete slabs. The hotbed is ventilated by pulling down the plastic film from the top and fastening it with clothespins.

Place a subbase of 6 inches of gravel and 4 inches of sand in the hotbed. Use at least 3 inches of good soil over the gravel-sand base. Be sure soil is free of weed seed and diseases.

Your county extension agent can give you information about sterilization of the soil. He can also help you with testing the soil.

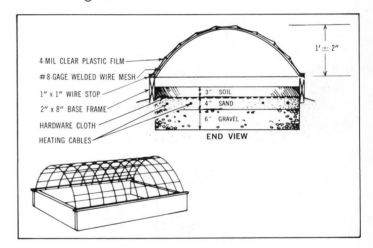

■ Use your electric drill to mix a small batch of concrete in a 5-gallon can with a T-shaped rod attachment. To make the mixer rod, weld an 8-inch crosspiece onto the bottom of a 2-foot length of ½-inch rod.

■ To cut metal roofing and siding when building a shed, a cutter made from a discarded one-man saw blade works well. File the back of the blade for a cutting edge and attach a long handle.

Angle iron base to which blade is fastened is divided so that blade fits between groove during cutting, thus giving support to both sides of metal. Cutter is mounted on 2 x 12 plank and set on saw-horses during use.

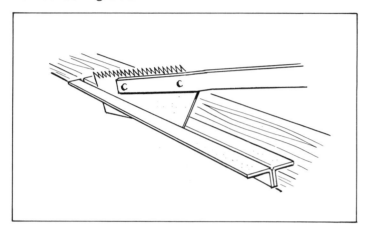

■ To keep swinging doors open on a gusty day, make a stop from short lengths of 2 x 4's. Attach a magnetic cabinet latch so the stop can easily be flipped up out of the way when not in use.

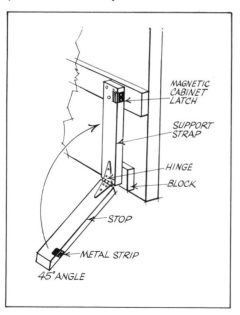

MAGNETIC CABINET LATCH

SUPPORT STRAP

HINGE

BLOCK

STOP

METAL STRIP

45° ANGLE

■ The problem of putting up some 18-foot 2 x 8 rafters was solved by this extension on the front-end loader of a tractor.

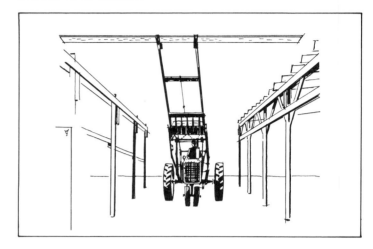

■ This pumphouse uses an old 16-can milk cooler box for the walls. This allows plenty of room inside for making minor repairs. The front is made so it can be removed completely when more work space is needed.

■ Post hole digger on back of tractor made quick work of digging trench for footing of milking parlor. Holes were bored a foot apart and loose dirt shoveled out of trench by hand.

■ When you have no help to lift the end of a long joist and hold it in place, and when it's not practical to use a strip of wood as support, try a heavy nail as a substitute. Drive the nail into the joist as shown.

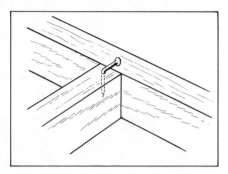

■ This oversized "sawhorse" raises wallboard to the ceiling at the turn of a crank. It holds the panel snugly against the joists so it can be nailed in position without a helper.

The rail is made of two 2 x 8's spaced so the 2 x 4 uprights of the elevator can move up and down between them. This particular model was built for a 7-foot, 9-inch ceiling.

The ⅛-inch flexible cable that hoists the elevator winds up on the shaft of the crank. It's anchored by a U-bolt through the shaft.

Springs between the cable and bottom crosspiece give enough so that you can slide the panel around.

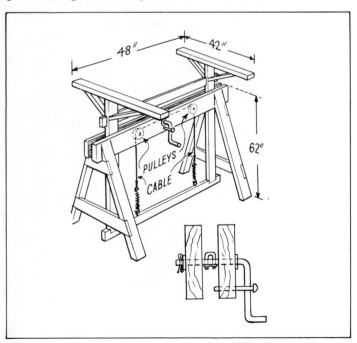

■ One person can open the roof on this pumphouse to get at the pump for repairs. To build, set four posts in the ground—one at each corner of the roof. Through these posts and the ends of the rafters, put a 1-inch pipe. This serves as a hinge. Roofing material on the ridge is fastened only to one side of the roof. This side must be opened first.

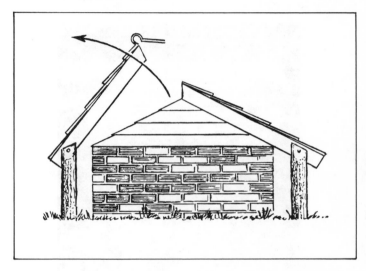

■ Four-inch iron pipe set in the concrete drive approach to storage building protects doors and door jambs.

■ Large swivel caster on top end of ladder used for roofwork makes it easier to get ladder into position at ridge and back down again.

Carpentry & Woodworking

■ Keep extra saw blades, table inserts, wrenches, and the miter gauge handy by mounting them on the side of your saw stand. A piece of plywood bolted to the stand serves as a tool board for the various brackets needed.

■ Tool holders on workshop sawhorse increase its usefulness. Here's how to adapt your own sawhorse: 1) Cut a slot in end of sawhorse to hold handsaw. 2) Nail a piece of grooved flooring on side of sawhorse to hold square. 3) With strip of leather, rubber, or covered wire, make loop for holding hammer.

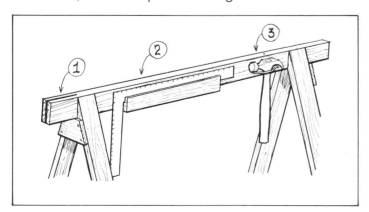

■ Touch-up sharpening of circular blade is quickly done without removing blade from arbor. To do this, raise blade as high as possible. Grip with C-clamps or locking-jaw pliers to keep from turning. Be sure power is off. Mark starting point with chalk, then use file with a light touch to "point" each tooth. Be careful to file at proper angle.

Don't try to "sharpen" blade—just hit peak of each tooth once or twice. Take blade to an expert if teeth are extremely dull or need resetting.

■ To keep from losing your pencil in the workshop, tie it to a string with a weight on the end. When you let go of the pencil, the weight pulls it up out of the way.

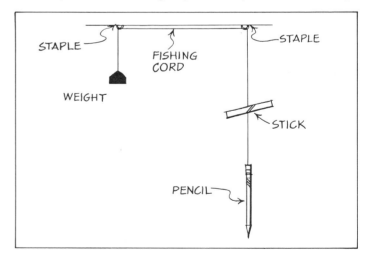

■ A discarded barber chair may not be the easiest thing to get your hands on, but it makes a good mount for a bench saw. It rotates 360 degrees and locks in place.

■ Chip guard of heavy plastic is a better-than-nothing substitute for blade guards discarded by many owners of power saws. This guard is held in place with a thumbscrew so it can be swung completely out of the way or removed easily. Bracket that holds guard is fastened to miter gauge.

■ Cutter from a pencil sharpener makes good attachment to use on drill press for dressing lumber. Shank for inserting into chuck is made by welding 16-penny nail in place. Attachment also works well for straight edges.

■ Drilling holes an inch or more in diameter often causes splitting of wood. One way to prevent this is to drill a guide hole. Use a drill slightly smaller than screw portion of the bit.

■ A small C-clamp will serve in place of a larger and more expensive woodworking clamp when used with two offset angles, as shown. Make angles from cold rolled steel. After locking in vise, bend without heating.

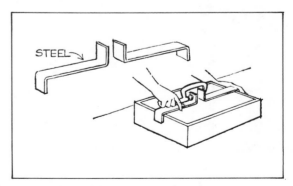

■ To remove boards held by stubborn screws or nails, cut teeth in a ½-inch steel tube and drill the plug over the screw.

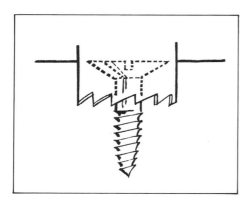

■ This adjustable marking gauge is improvised from a turnbuckle, yardstick, and compass pencil holder. It's especially useful on wide panels of plywood or hardboard, and is adaptable for marking large circles.

The pencil holder, removed from a 10-cent store compass, is bolted to end of the yardstick. The yardstick is shortened ¼ inch on this end, so that measurements will be accurate.

Inside bottom edge of the turnbuckle is filed flat to make the guide. Top eyebolt is filed flat on the bottom. Lower eyebolt is removed. Turnbuckle is then slipped over yardstick and the eyebolt tightened at whatever distance from the end you wish.

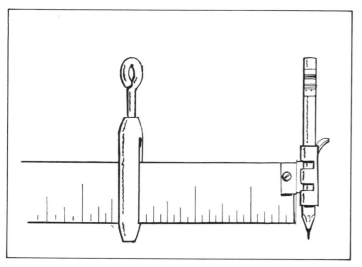

■ To keep marking pencil sharp, mount a pencil sharpener from the dime store in the handle of your square. Glue holds it in place.

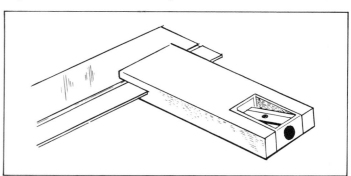

■ Keep blade clean and sharp to keep circular power saw from stalling and at cutting peak. Give teeth touch-up sharpening before each sawing session. When blade gets rough or gummy, smooth with wad of steel wool stuffed into suitable holder. A 35mm. film can, made of soft aluminum, is a good holder. Use kerosene or mineral spirits as a solvent.

■ Use a piece of light chain fastened to the ceiling joists of your shop to hold various projects while the finish is drying. An 8-penny finish nail driven into one edge of the shelves, doors, or other flat pieces and then bent to form a hook will hold them on the chain. The links of chain will keep the pieces from sliding together as they would if hung on rope or wire.

■ Screws hold tight in the end grain of soft wood or plywood and make a stronger joint if they are driven into a dowel that fits in hole drilled at right angle to screws. Glue dowels in place and drill pilot holes for screws.

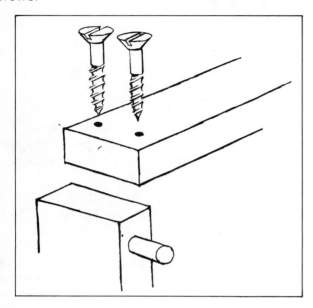

■ Finishing nails make satisfactory substitutes for small woodworking drills. Just clip off the head, flatten the end with a hammer, then fasten tightly in the chuck.

■ To hold blade steady while sharpening circle saw, make a simple clamp with two lengths of 2-inch lumber, each 2½ feet long. Blade goes between these two boards and is held tight by a ½-inch bolt. Just loosen the nut one turn when you want to move the saw.

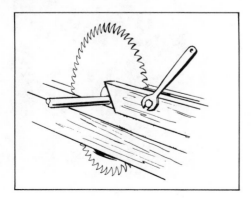

■ When hanging cabinet doors, use a jig to save measuring time and to get pulls, knobs, or hinges equally spaced.

This one is made from a piece of plywood about 4 inches wide and 16 inches long. Narrow (½-inch) strips of wood are fastened on both sides along two edges. Holes are drilled in the proper position so that when you fit the device tightly against the corner of each door, you can quickly mark the place where you want holes drilled in the door.

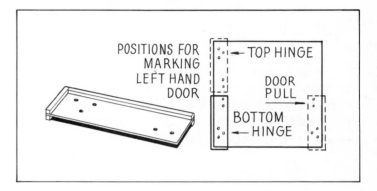

■ A wider than usual plank for the top rail of this sawhorse provides a handier work surface than the usual 2 x 4. The tray below is for small tools, nails, or screws. A 2-inch strip of wood on each side of the tray keeps tools from being jarred off during sawing or hammering.

Chapter VII
arounD THe Farm

Fuel Storage

■ The tank truck operator appreciates the ladder on this fuel storage tank. Metal rod bent to triangular shape and welded to one leg of frame forms steps and hand holds. Note that the leg on which steps are welded extends above tank top.

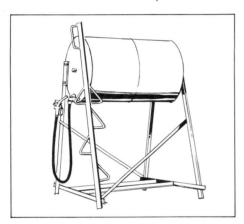

■ This is a good way to lock a 55-gallon drum which has a hand pump. Most hand fuel pumps have a place for a lock. Link a short piece of chain from lock to an eyebolt welded in a ¾-inch pipe nipple and back to the lock. When locked like this, neither pump nor nipple can be screwed out.

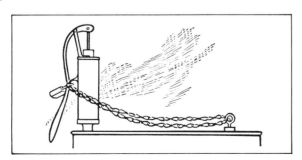

■ An ordinary yardstick can be used to measure how much oil or other liquid is left in a regular 55-gallon drum. Mark measurements with notches, because oil will dissolve printing on the stick.

Figure 5 gallons to each 2⅞ inches in depth when the drum is standing on end. Use figures below for estimating contents when drum is on its side.

5 Gallons	3⅜ inches
10 Gallons	5⅜ inches
15 Gallons	7⅛ inches
20 Gallons	8⅞ inches
25 Gallons	10⅜ inches
30 Gallons	12 inches
35 Gallons	13½ inches
40 Gallons	15⅛ inches
45 Gallons	16⅞ inches
50 Gallons	18¾ inches
55 Gallons (full)	21½ inches

■ Adding sides to the fuel stand transforms it into a storage shed for grease and oil. A door with lock can easily be added.

■ Leave a spring clothespin on the fuel tank stand so the deliveryman can clip the delivery ticket where the farm operator will find it. This is also a handy place for leaving notes for the deliveryman in case you think of special supplies he carries on his truck that you forgot to order. This frees you and your family to go about your work without having to watch for the tank truck.

■ Cutoff valve on fuel tank mounted too high to reach comfortably is opened and closed with an extension lever operated from the ground. Rack is built from frame of junked windmill. Tankman reaches tank by climbing ladder built into one of the legs. At top is platform built of expanded metal for him to stand on.

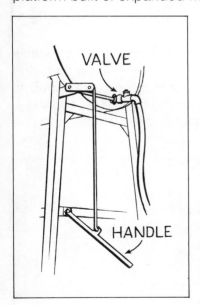

VALVE

HANDLE

■ To lock a faucet and barrel, use a ½-inch U-bolt through the air cap to hold a piece of strap iron that locks at the faucet. Then you need have no fear of anyone getting gas or oil out of your drum.

Pipes & Underground Lines

■ Pull metal pipe from well with notched ½- x 4-inch angle iron that grips pipe as you raise tractor front-end loader. Angle iron is about 8 inches long. It is hung by one end from chain attached to loader. Notch should be just large enough to fit around pipe. A second piece of notched angle iron is used to hold pipe as you drop front-end loader to get another grip.

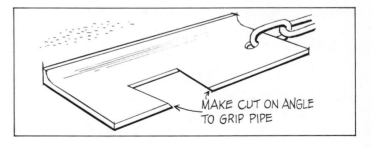

MAKE CUT ON ANGLE TO GRIP PIPE

■ Insulating water pipes with discarded garden watering hose keeps water lines from freezing. Cut ¾-inch hose to right length, split it with a knife, and slip it over ½-inch water lines.

■ An easy way to lay pipe or underground lines is to use a tractor-mounted subsoiler. Here are several ideas:

Pipe collar (size of pipe desired) welded to a strap and bolted to the rear of subsoiler point will pull pipe into ground at least 18 inches deep. Dig a rather long trench for pipe to feed into ground so as not to bend it too short. In hard ground run subsoiler along the trail several times before hooking to pipe so as not to encounter obstacles underground.

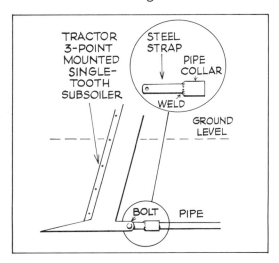

By attaching a piece of 1½-inch pipe about 40 inches long to the back of subsoiler, ¾-inch plastic pipe or wire can be laid and covered 18 to 26 inches in one operation, depending on condition of soil. One or two trial runs should be made to loosen soil. One helper should walk behind tractor to hold and feed plastic pipe into attached galvanized pipe.

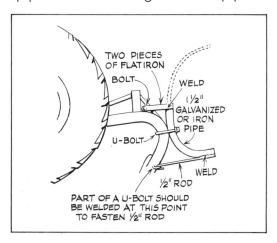

Pipe can be pulled underground by attaching it to the subsoiler with a short length of pipe bent and drilled to form a hitch. A hitch can be made from a piece of pipe about 15 inches long. Flatten it on one end and bend at almost a right angle. A hole is drilled in this so it can be attached to subsoiler with the bottom bolt of the subsoiler point. Pipe is fastened to hitch with a regular coupling.

Before you start laying the pipe, drive the subsoiler a time or two along the path where you want the pipeline. At the beginning of the line, dig a ditch the depth the line is to be and about 6 feet longer than one joint of pipe.

Whenever the line is pulled forward enough to give room to work in the ditch, stop the tractor and couple another joint of pipe.

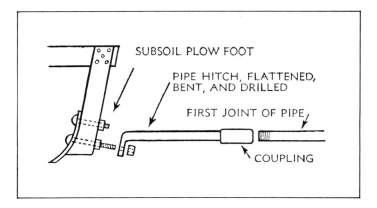

You can lay underground electrical cable with a modified subsoiler similar to the type used for laying plastic pipe. Cable is fed through pipe fastened to back of subsoiler, as shown in sketch. This cable-laying device is quick to make and easily attached to a farm tractor.

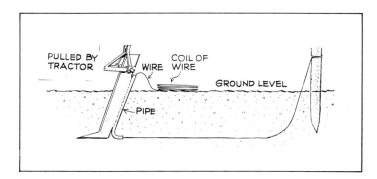

■ You can put a 2-inch water line under a road without tearing up the road surface by pushing pipe under the road with a bulldozer.

To keep from bending the pipe, use 4-foot lengths of pipe instead of one long length. Cap the first length, then ease the bulldozer against the pipe and push it under the road as far as possible. Then connect 4 more feet and push it under.

■ The next time you have to dig up tile to clean out sewer line, run a heavy wire through the tile and through the line. Tie it firmly to an iron stake at each end of the line. Then, when you have to clean the sewer again, you can open the line at each end, fasten a big chain to the wire and pull it back and forth through the line a few times.

Ponds, Wells, & Irrigation

■ Increase water supply for dairy and household by using siphon to connect two shallow wells. When pumping starts from the one well, siphoning begins automatically and continues until both wells have the same water level.

To make priming simple, install a faucet at pump, as shown, and use heavy-duty garden hose in the well from which you pump. The rest of the siphon is made from plastic pipe. Line is filled by attaching hose to faucet.

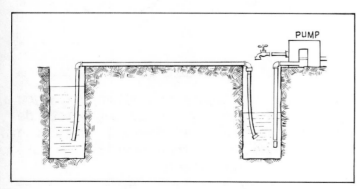

PUMP

■ A float on the end of the suction pipe of an irrigation rig that draws water from a pond or stream keeps end of the pipe off the bottom where it's likely to draw in mud and debris. An inner tube tied on with rope works fine.

■ Irrigation trailer hauls 800 feet of 4-inch pipe and one large sprinkler head that is permanently mounted near center of trailer. Sprinkler is on an 8-foot riser of 3-inch pipe.

With this rig you can water four acres of tobacco a day in just four moves. No leaf is damaged if field is laid out so irrigation trailer (as well as dusters and sprayers) can travel unplanted rows and never have to go through crop. Trailer is pulled with a tractor. Hitch is at opposite end of inlet pipe, which also is permanently mounted.

Trailer bed is 14 feet long and 44 inches wide. Upright at ends and center of each side hold pipe in place when transporting. On each side, braces of ½-inch rod go from top of center upright to both ends.

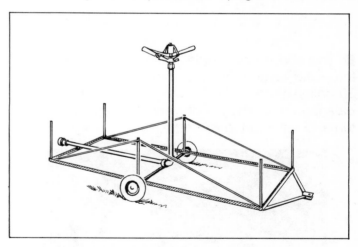

■ Snakes in your pond can be attracted to one spot for easy capturing. Dig a hole in the bank 2 or 3 feet from edge of the water. Hole should be 2 or 3 inches deep and 10 to 12 inches wide. Cover with a board, but leave half-inch opening so snakes can crawl under. Very often in the summertime, you may turn up the board and find a snake under it.

■ The overflow pipe on your stock tank won't get clogged when using this device. A short length of larger pipe is placed over the regular overflow pipe. It extends about four inches above the overflow and about 12 inches below water level. This trash guard is held in place by three small rods welded from top of the overflow to top of guard, and also by three spacers at the bottom.

Overflow water enters guard 12 inches below floating trash.

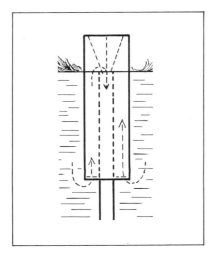

■ This above-water turtle trap raises and lowers with the water level. It is built from an old inner tube, a 50-gallon drum, and some 2 x 4's. The center board is balanced so that it tips with very little load, causing the turtle to fall into the drum.

■ A light rigged to run off the generator of the engine in irrigation well house is very handy. Since it is on only when the pump is running, you can look out the window at night and easily tell if the engine has run out of fuel or has died for some other reason. The light is also a safety factor when you go into the wellhouse to check oil and switches.

To install, wire in an automotive-type bulb—one wire to the armature terminal on the generator and the other grounded to the motor.

Try a similar idea with a deep well pump: wire a light bulb into the circuit of the pump so that the bulb is lit whenever the pump should be running. If pump runs longer than it normally does, you can check to see what's wrong and can detect trouble before the motor burns out.

■ Bottom of water storage tank will not be damaged as tank settles if flexible coupling is used instead of solid lead-down pipe. A 30-inch length of radiator hose clamped in place takes care of a 15-inch gap.

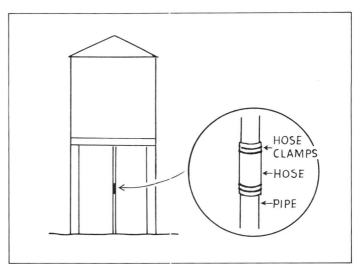

■ When your water supply is cut off temporarily, you can get water from another source through an outside spigot. This calls for the needed length of hose and an extra fitting from the hardware store, so you have identical fittings on each end.

■ Jumper cables from pickup battery can be used to start irrigation engines. To eliminate the constant raising and lowering of the hood and the many times when you don't make a good connection the first time, install some electric welder cable plug-ins on the pickup and on one end of each cable. Just plug in the cables and they're ready to go. Mount the plug-ins on a bracket that fits in the grill of the pickup and paint one set of connectors red and the other black to eliminate any mixup between positive and negative.

■ To run only clean water into cistern from the barn roof, use a downspout that empties into a covered 55-gallon drum. First few minutes of rain fills drum and downspout up to inlet pipes, which then run clean water into concrete cistern. Steel drum has a slow leak that drains it in 24 hours. Then it's ready for another rain.

■ When the pressure hits the end of the irrigation line and unhooks it just after you've made a move—and moves the line a few inches apart—rehooking the entire line from separation to end is no fun. Solve the problem by making a short pipe, about a foot long, with coupling and hook that is kept at the pump. It can be used to rehook at the separation easily just by curving the line a small amount. Damaged pipes can be used for this purpose.

■ If you need to work oxygen into the water of a catfish pond quickly and have no pump or other aerator available on a short notice, use a rotary cutter to agitate the water.

■ This "dry-weather bridge" stays in place when stream goes on a rampage. Water passes harmlessly over the top, rather than taking bridge with it.
  Culverts for normal stream flow were formed by putting metal drums (ends removed) in place before pouring concrete for roadway.

■ When end of overflow pipe in your pond is covered with water and pipe becomes clogged, the obstruction can usually be cleared by plugging outlet end of pipe, letting pipe fill with water, then quickly removing plug. Force created by head of flowing water will usually clear obstruction and draw it through pipe.

■ A water pump from a junked car can be used for irrigation or drainage. It can easily be primed through the car heater plug on the pump. The pump is powered by a ¾-hp gasoline engine from an old lawn mower. Pump and motor are mounted on separate boards. That way they can be put together with the right spacing for almost any size V belt.

■ Overshot wheel, fashioned after mill wheel of bygone days, is a useful novelty. Overflow from pond keeps large grindstone turning constantly so there are few excuses for dull tools. Shaft is mounted in bearings with grease fittings.

■ Water rescue equipment for a farm pond can be made with a strong fishing pole and a length of light rope. This rope should be twice as long as the pole, and taped or tied to the pole every foot or so. Small piece of lightweight, floatable material should be tied to the loose end. To rescue a person, throw the line with the pole (as in fishing) and then pull out as if it were only a rope.

Stump & Tree Removal

■ Sprout control is automatic if you use a mixture of brush killer and oil in your chain saw oiler. Useful when clearing hardwoods, this idea works especially well for girdling where sprouting or quick kill is a factor.

■ To move heavy objects around the farm, make skids by curving 30- x 48-inch sections of steel plate and drilling holes in each corner. Steel cable is threaded through holes as shown in sketch. After skid is loaded, loop short piece of chain around cables near center of skid so that chain and cables secure load when skid is towed. Ends of skid are notched for easier handling of logs.

■ Adding air pressure to a tank of herbicide mounted on the back of a jeep helps to keep under control new growth of mesquite.

Put about 35 gallons of herbicide in a 42-gallon tank, then add about 60 pounds' air pressure. Two pliable rubber hoses, each about 10 feet long, are attached to tank. At the end of each hose is a hand-nozzle and about 3 feet of copper tubing slightly curved at the end.

With two people in the jeep, it is an easy job to kill out a 20- to 25-foot strip. The driver alone can manage a 10-foot strip without getting out.

■ A soft-core, ⅝-inch wire cable can be used instead of chain for pulling stumps and other heavy loads. A chain is used for wrapping around the object to be pulled, but it is a winch-line tail chain that is designed for heavy-duty use. This is attached to the end of the cable by passing the cable through one link and fastening with two ⅜-inch cable clamps. Take at least two wraps around the object to be pulled, then slip the hook over the cable. The grip tightens as you pull.

A small loop on the tractor end of the cable allows it to be attached to the drawbar with a standard clevis.

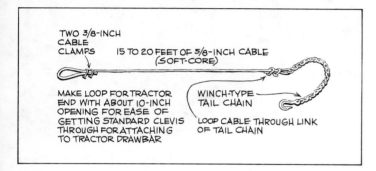

TWO 3/8-INCH CABLE CLAMPS
15 TO 20 FEET OF 5/8-INCH CABLE (SOFT-CORE)
MAKE LOOP FOR TRACTOR END WITH ABOUT 10-INCH OPENING FOR EASE OF GETTING STANDARD CLEVIS THROUGH FOR ATTACHING TO TRACTOR DRAWBAR
WINCH-TYPE TAIL CHAIN
LOOP CABLE THROUGH LINK OF TAIL CHAIN

■ The harder you pull, the tighter this chain puller grips tree, brush, or post. This keeps it from slipping off. To build it, use a piece of pipe about 18 inches long and from 2 to 4 inches across. On the side, flush with one end, weld a chain hook of the proper size for the chain to be used. To use, secure one end of chain to drawbar, run other end through pipe and around tree, and fasten it in hook, as shown in sketch.

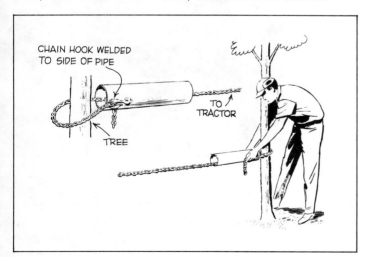

CHAIN HOOK WELDED TO SIDE OF PIPE
TO TRACTOR
TREE

■ This bush and small tree puller can be made to mount on a tractor's three-point hitch. Just back the tractor against the tree while lift pressure is applied. It uproots trees up to 6 inches in diameter.

Bottom edges of the bars must have a turned-in shape in order to grip what you are pulling. To obtain the rolled edge, heat the steel and bend the edge inward over an anvil. Grind the rolled edge to smooth out rough spots and sharpen it just enough that it digs into the wood but doesn't shear the tree off completely.

Top edge of the pulling bar may be sharpened by beveling instead of leaving it square. The sharpened top edge is used to slide the bar under the roots to break them, making uprooting easier.

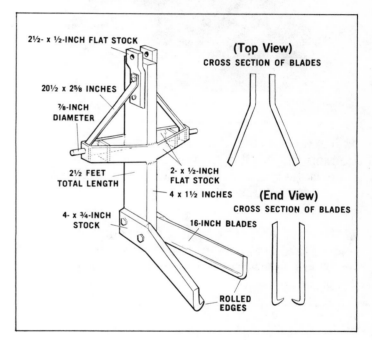

2½- x ½-INCH FLAT STOCK
20½ x 2⅝ INCHES
⅞-INCH DIAMETER
2½ FEET TOTAL LENGTH
4- x ¾-INCH STOCK
2- x ½-INCH FLAT STOCK
4 x 1½ INCHES
16-INCH BLADES
ROLLED EDGES
(Top View) CROSS SECTION OF BLADES
(End View) CROSS SECTION OF BLADES

■ Burning stumps takes little effort when you make use of 55-gallon drums with both ends cut out. Set drum over stump, with stones under rim to allow good draft. Soak stump with 1-quart fuel oil and 1-quart waste motor oil before setting afire. Medium-sized stumps will burn out overnight.

■ Poisoning undesirable hardwood trees with liquid poison after frilling trunk with axe is an easy, one-man job when you use a tree marking gun to squirt poison in frill. Carry gun by hanging it on stiff wire hook attached to belt. This idea works especially well when trees are scattered.

■ To reduce the danger of spreading fire when burning brush piles, wait until after a heavy rain to burn. In the meantime keep them covered with a large sheet of plastic, so they will be dry.

■ To clear land of trees, first run a subsoiler around each tree to cut its roots. This makes it easier to push up. A subsoiler also is useful to remove stumps of smaller trees.

General Tips

■ To protect outside lock from the weather, tack a piece of leather just above it. A 6- x 8-inch piece usually is large enough to cover lock. This is especially helpful in freezing rain or snow. Leather can easily be raised so you can get at the lock.

■ Shoe cleaner was built from scrap parts found on the farm. Scraper is 12-inch length of angle iron with a No. 3 horseshoe welded to each end. Two scrub-brushes, facing in, are attached with wood screws to tops of horseshoes. Legs welded to bottom are set in concrete.

■ When in the field, this chain saw is used to fill spray tanks on tractor. It powers a pump that fills the two 55-gallon barrels on the tractor in about four minutes. Just replace the chain sprocket with a belt pulley. Converting the saw back to use for timber cutting takes just a few minutes.

■ Keep tarpaulins tight by fastening them to truck with rubber bands cut from old tire inner tube. Cut bands about 1 inch wide. Fasten one end to tarp loop or through grommet and stretch other end over hook near bed of truck. This not only makes a faster, neater job but keeps wind from tearing tarp.

■ This rotary firefighter effectively snuffs out grass fires. Water in the handle-mounted tank keeps the drum wet. Sand or water can be used in the drum to increase the weight if desired.

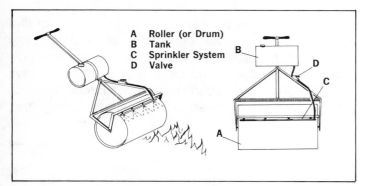

A   Roller (or Drum)
B   Tank
C   Sprinkler System
D   Valve

■ A barn door track and roller carry the auger on the feed grinder and make it easy to put the auger in and take it out of bins. In operating position the auger is directly over the mill. Remove a hold-down pin and it swings to transport and storage position where it is pinned in place. Reinforcements under the mixer top are necessary for bolting on the brackets.

■ You can seed grass at the same time you spread chicken litter, thus making your spreader do double duty. Just mix grass seed with litter in the house before you load it on the spreader.

■ Plywood flaps keep tall stepladders from tipping. Made from ⅜- or ½-inch plywood, they are especially helpful when stepladder is set on soft earth, as when you are picking fruit. Use two or three hinges under the flaps so they can be folded over front of the ladder for ease in carrying and storing.

■ These saddle racks will store four saddles, blankets, and bridles in only 1 square yard of floor space. Dimensions are not critical and can be varied to take advantage of scrap metal on hand.

■ Use coated fiber glass cloth to seal opening where auger enters grain storage bin. Fiber glass and the adhesive coating, epoxy resin mixed with hardener, form a seal that is waterproof and ratproof. This seal is metal-hard when dry, but is easy to work into desired shape. Material for such a seal comes in repair kits for boats and automobile bodies. Adhesive coating also is excellent for joining canvas boot around auger that comes off bottom of feed storage hopper.

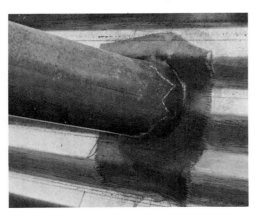

■ To remove broken handle from head of axe, bore hole through wood in eye of axe. Handle can be pounded out easier, and there's no need for burning and damaging the temper of the axe.

Center hole carefully, if using wood auger, so you won't dull or break it.

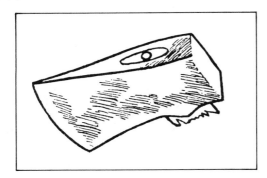

■ Grain bin from an old combine makes a good storage bin for feed. Welding bin to stand made of pipe speeds hand-feeding.

■ Grade and pack vegetables at the farmstead, load them onto the display platform, then pull the whole thing with a tractor to the stand's usual location beside the highway. At the end of the day pull it back to the yard.

Running gear is a heavy farm wagon. Floor of the wagon forms the display platform. Scale and cashbox at rear are protected by wide roof overhang, which extends several feet over sides and ends of display. Normal frame construction with 2-inch lumber is used for the roof. It is covered with solid decking and corrugated roofing.

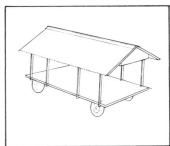

■ Placing a 2- x 6-inch board, with small logging chain attached, under rear wheels will often help free stuck farm equipment.

Use chains with hooks on both ends. If hooks are large enough, place them on end of board away from tires; if not large enough, attach chains to boards as shown in illustration.

If boards are properly placed, tire treads will crawl up chains like link chains on a sprocket.

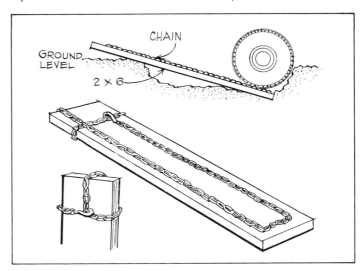

■ Screen door springs attached to bed of lime trucks can hook into eyelets on covering tarps and keep covers down firmly on the road, even in high winds. This little trick is a moneysaver, especially on long hauls, where windship "unloads" a lot of limestone along the route.

■ Rust-resistant paint works well for marking crowbars, shovels, tamping bars, wrenches, and other farm tools. Contrasting colors make the tools easy to spot in tall grass or on plowed ground.

■ This "blue jay" trap is made from 1-inch poultry mesh. Ends are fastened by wrapping wire around selvage. Temporary fastening is used at one corner so friendly birds or animals can be released easily. Bait is a trail of corn leading into trap.

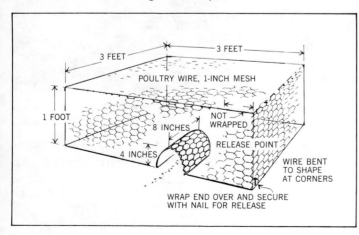

■ Wooden table legs that stand on damp floors can be kept from rotting by keeping them off the floor with short lengths of pipe. Pieces of pipe are stuck in holes drilled several inches deep in ends of legs.

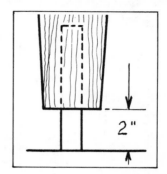

■ To keep pitchforks handy but out of the way, spot fork holders at several convenient places around the barn. Each holder is made from a 6-inch length of garden hose split down the middle. This is nailed in place so it keeps fork from falling when handle is snapped into holder.

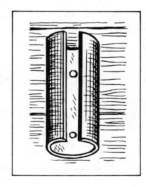

■ When hauling water in a barrel or container that has no lid, place on top of the water a thin board about half the diameter of container. Then water will not spill as easily.

■ Farmers can make use of enclosed truck boxes no longer used by trucking companies. Many dealers trade for a chassis only, but on occasion get the whole unit and then have an opportunity to sell only the used chassis. Building a weathertight shelter from a used truck box is cheaper than building the shelter from scratch.

■ An old disk forms the base for this portable foot scraper. It's safer than the usual scraper fastened along the walk, because children are not as apt to fall on it or trip over it. The crosspiece at top serves as a handle, so the scraper can be moved easily out of the way during dry weather.

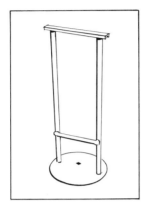

■ To figure the acreage of a field quickly, measure the width and length with your tractor.

A piece of white cloth slipped over the valve of a rear tire makes it easy to count turns of the wheel.

Since there are 100 links in a chain and 10 square chains in an acre, the job is easy, now that you've measured and found that the rear wheel travels 18.4 links each revolution. (One link is 7.92 inches; a chain equals 66 feet. This measurement is in multiples of 10 and easy to figure.)

Multiplying the distance covered in one turn by the number of turns and dividing by 100 gives you the width or length in chains. (That's the same as multiplying the number of turns by .184.) Multiplying width times length gives the number of square chains.

■ Keep a box of baking soda in your car and another in your truck for use in case of a small fire. Baking soda is an excellent fire extinguisher and does not harm the motor.

■ For safe storage of insecticides, pesticides, and dangerous small tools on the farm, move old, unusable metal grain bin to a convenient location. Place sign on front to remind adults to be careful. The lock keeps children out.

■ To cut back long blackberry briars, use a pole pruner that normally is used on fruit tree limbs. This lets you trim out around shrubs without the misery of getting thorns in your hands.

■ This bumper, foam rubber tightly wound on end of light wooden handle, is excellent for thinning peaches. Six to eight sharp blows are enough to thin four- to five-year-old trees. And it takes less than one-half minute per tree.

About 15 blows are needed for six- to eight-year-old trees and 25 to 30 for older trees. In most cases, a quick touchup by hand or by the old pole-thinning method may also be needed. Trees are not damaged.

Bumper is started by nailing a long section of heavy inner tube and a 12- x 18-inch piece of 4-inch foam rubber to end of pole. Foam rubber and inner tube are then tightly rolled around the handle. Last few turns of the inner tube section are completed after the foam rubber is completely covered. Strong pulling on the inner tube continues to compress the foam rubber. Large-headed nails and twine secure the inner tube.

■ Sewer-cleaning rod with handmade spear or hook on end unclogs blower pipe when filling upright silo.

■ This waterer for tiny quail attracts birds to water, but offers no chance for accidental drowning of birds. It is made from a quart glass jar with metal lid. Water comes out through a hole in center of lid. Young birds are attracted by glitter of water droplet in this hole, which is about the size of a BB shot, and get water when they peck at it.

■ Extra weight of handle made from pipe makes it easy to jab shovel into hard ground, sandstone, and gravel. To make, saw wooden handle at top of steel neck of "sharpshooter." Then slip 3 or 4 feet of 1½-inch pipe over neck.

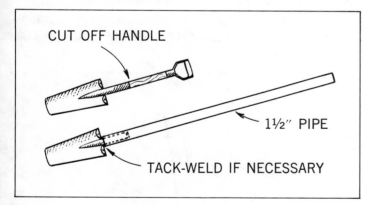

CUT OFF HANDLE

1½" PIPE

TACK-WELD IF NECESSARY

■ Emergency outside lighting for areas where you usually don't work at night can be rigged up quickly by taping socket and extension cord to the handle of a pitchfork. Put a reflector on the light; then you can stick fork in ground at any angle to direct light where you want it.

■ A farm spotlight adjustable to almost any angle is easily built. First set a post in the ground. Mount a 110-volt spotlight bulb with weatherproof socket on an 18-inch length of 1 by 4 which is pivoted on the end of a pole or length of pipe. After bolting on control lever and control rod, mount pole to post with iron straps. Control lever moves light around or up and down. Switch may be mounted on post. Use weatherproof cord left loose enough to make one complete turn.

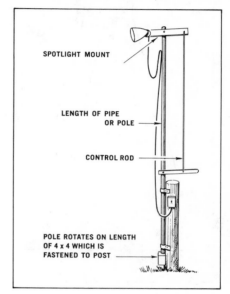

SPOTLIGHT MOUNT

LENGTH OF PIPE OR POLE

CONTROL ROD

POLE ROTATES ON LENGTH OF 4 x 4 WHICH IS FASTENED TO POST

■ A nonslip clevis for chains can be made by anyone with access to a welder. Cut two short pieces of iron rod on a bevel and weld them just inside the bow of the tractor clevis. Leave enough space to hold a chain link.

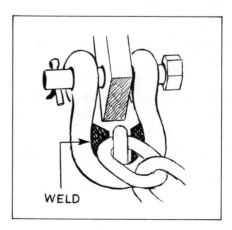

WELD

■ This pipe stand was built to support a grain elevator. It's made from used galvanized pipe. All joints are welded. The center pipe swings freely on the cross-piece so that height of the elevator can be adjusted easily.

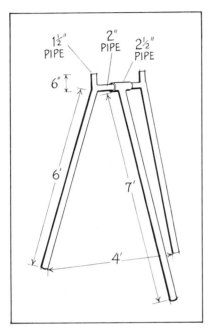

■ Thinning peaches by hand is faster if limbs just out of reach are pulled down with a hook and held down by standing on rubber hose clamped to hook. Three-foot piece of ¼-inch iron rod or heavy copper tubing is good for making the hook. Shape it by bending around a 2-inch pipe. Old air hose—3 or 4 feet of it—should be clamped securely to straight end of rod or tubing.

This gadget will also save ladder time and lessen bruising.

■ To start Bermuda grass in gullies and other difficult places, fill a burlap bag with sod. Soak the bag, and knead it into place. The bag holds the Bermuda in place and keeps it moist until rooted. Grass grows right through the burlap, which soon rots away.

■ A white shirt or other light-colored cloth can be useful if you get caught out on a dark night with a flat tire and no flashlight. Have someone hold the garment close to, and almost directly in front of, the headlight. Enough light to work by will be reflected.

■ A wire brush usually wears out first on the front end. Since the handle is of wood, simply saw off the worn-off end (between rows of steel strands) and you have a good brush again. This can be done several times on the same brush.

■ Add more foot power to spades, shovels, and spreading forks by welding a short section of angle iron to the upper edge. This provides plenty of pushing surface for your foot and makes the digging job a lot less tiring.

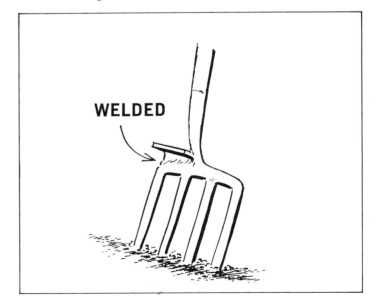

■ By taking the diggers off tiller and replacing them with a set of home-built wheels, you can use tiller to pull a laying-off plow or a cultivator.

■ For more comfort at mealtime in the field when custom combining, put a large tractor umbrella on the car bumper. An umbrella with pole at the edge rather than in the center works best. Mount stand on bumper permanently so umbrella can easily be slipped into stand as soon as car is stopped in the field. Umbrella stand is set on bumper hitch mounted upside down, so braces fit onto bumper bolts without change.

■ Old fertilizer bags now can be put to good use on your farm. Disposing of them used to be quite a problem, but now save them and place them on the ground in your hay barn before storing hay. They are made of water-resistant material and do a good job of protecting hay from direct contact with the ground.

■ Torn clothes and scratches will be avoided if you sheathe your fishhooks with pencil erasers. Erasers are pliable enough to accommodate several hook sizes.

■ Protect light switches in barns and farm shops from accidental breakage by using guards made of strap iron. Bend cold in vise so guards are an inch or more out from switch.

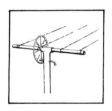

Chapter VIII

around the Home

General Household Tips

■ Front-end loader on tractor is an excellent substitute for scaffolding when painting the family home. Adjust it to any height needed. It's faster and easier than moving a ladder.

■ Heavy barn door handles (pulls), placed on door facings, on walls near chairs, in the bathroom, and other places where elderly people could use a helping hand, prevent many falls. Pulls can be painted to match walls and woodwork or left black so they can be seen easily.

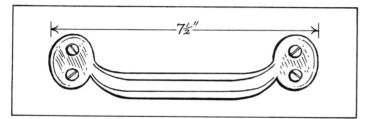

■ Woodbox in wall beside fireplace saves tracking through house when put in outside wall so it can be filled from outside. If outside opening is put under carport, it can be filled even in a heavy rain. Box should be large enough to hold 24-hour supply of wood. Eight-inch board across front of box keeps wood from rolling out. To give appearance of built-in cabinet, build box as far out into room as front of fireplace, close inside opening with double doors, and build bookshelves in space over box.

OUTSIDE OPENING

■ Problems with TV lead-in cable breakage and poor reception during high winds can be lessened by running the lead-in through a ½-inch water hose clamped to the antenna support.

■ Keeping a last year's telephone book in the car or pickup can help locate even a local address when in town.

■ Trash cans are held on this rack by hooks on a 4-inch length of pipe that slips over center pipe and grips cans by their top rims. Practically dog-proof!

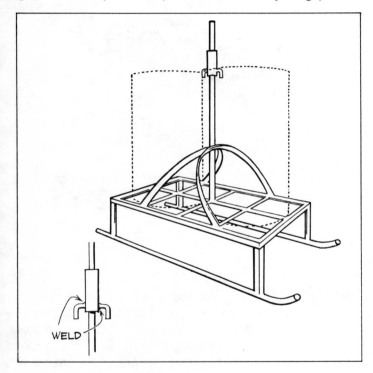

WELD

■ Protect windows when painting by covering with newspaper stuck on with rubber cement. If you're careful, the rubber cement alone will keep the glass clean. After paint dries, cement and dried paint may be rubbed off easily with fingertips. Rubber cement is available at stationery stores.

■ Steel wool placed in a can that has a few holes punched in the bottom makes a good paint strainer.

■ Strainers to eliminate trash from liquids can be added to funnels made from the tops of plastic bleach and detergent bottles. Use women's discarded nylon hose either stretched across top of funnel or stuffed loosely in funnel.

■ Outdoor cooking stand made from pipe and round rod comes apart for easy carrying. Legs should be made first. Then the two 3-foot pieces of round iron should be bent at right angles 3 inches from each end so they will fit into legs. Next, the ½-inch round bars on each end of the cooking platform are welded in place. This is most easily done by fitting turned-up ends of rod into legs and then turning upside down (legs sticking straight up) on flat surface to weld. Smaller rods are then welded 2 inches apart to make platform for cooking. Legs may be driven into ground to get desired height above fire.

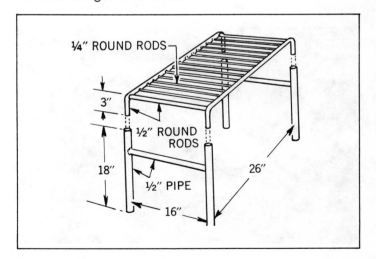

¼" ROUND RODS

3"

½" ROUND RODS

18"

½" PIPE

16"

26"

■ Plastic hand lotion bottle with a built-in pump makes a handy container for liquid shampoo. This one is hung from an overhead joist by wire looped around the neck of the bottle. Slipping a short length of plastic tubing over the spout makes it easier to use. One or two squirts is usually enough.

■ To keep metal clothesline poles from leaning, weld worn disk blades to the bottom before sinking them in the ground.

■ Mailbox support is 1½-inch pipe set in a 10-gallon milk can filled with concrete. Two bolts hold box on horizontal pipe that screws into pipe tee. Old disk from a harrow is welded to top of upright post. This is for large packages that cannot or should not be put in box. Hole in disk is left open so water can drain out through pipe.

■ Friends visiting at night will have little trouble finding your house if you have luminous roadside markers made from old harrow disks. Letter the dished-out (concave) sides of the disks with luminous paint, then bolt to wooden posts and set in ground by your driveway.

■ Here's how an ice cream freezer was converted from hand-operated to electric. First remove the hand crank from the freezer. Then couple it to the wringer drive from an old washing machine. The coupler merely connects the wringer drive unit to the shaft that drives the freezer. Powering the wringer drive with the washing machine motor turns the freezer about the same speed as turning it by hand. All pieces are securely mounted on a wooden platform.

■ Here's a good temporary fix for a swinging kitchen mixer faucet. Remove the worn rings, slip on rubber-bands of a size that would fit tight and flat under each O ring, then replace the old O rings.

■ Sagging clotheslines can easily be tightened by turning the wheel that's welded to pipe on which wires are fastened. This pipe fits inside a sleeve welded to top of the post. Small L-shaped rod a few inches below top of post catches one spoke of the wheel to keep wires tight. Rod is spring loaded so it springs back into locked position by itself whenever it's pulled out in order to turn the wheel.

■ This Christmas tree stand uses a gallon bucket, a piece of 4-inch pipe 2 inches longer than height of bucket, and cement. Place pipe (with screw holes drilled near upper end) upright in bucket, then fill bucket with cement. After cement sets, you can paint the bucket. When tree is set in pipe, screws tightened against trunk hold it firmly in place.

■ Problems of identification can be solved by adding a small identification tag and keyring to equipment. Tags can be made from old aluminum pots, lids, and other scraps that are available. Identifying marks are stamped in the tag itself.

■ Handy twine holder is made from discarded funnel. To add cutter, snip a slit and bend out tab, as shown. To help prevent accidental cuts, make sure funnel is mounted on wall so that tab points toward the rear.

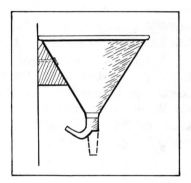

■ If you are repairing a leaky faucet and do not have the proper tool to reface the faucet seat, attach a disk of sandpaper or emery to a ⅝-inch-diameter wooden dowel rod with a roundhead wood screw. Select a size screw so that the head serves as a guide when dowel is inserted into seat and twirled between the palms until seat is free of worn or eroded spots. Drain water out of faucet, as it may cause the sandpaper to tear.

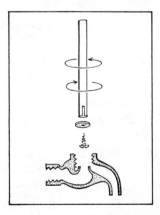

■ To thaw frozen pipes, use an old upright vacuum sweeper from which the bag has been removed. Attach a suction hose from a tank-type sweeper. Hot air from the outlet of your heating plant can be pumped to the frozen pipe. If the pipe is not readily accessible to a warm-air outlet, pull heat from a small electric heater.

Lawn & Garden Tips

■ To keep young shade trees from being damaged or twisted off by strong spring winds, brace them with hardwood branches. Braces should have considerable curve near the large end in order to tape this end securely to trunk of the tree and have braces extend upward in the direction you want branches to grow.

Before taping young branches lightly to these braces, braces should be wrapped to prevent injury to tender growth. When young branches have enough strength to stand on their own, remove braces so as not to have any girdling effect on trunk and branches.

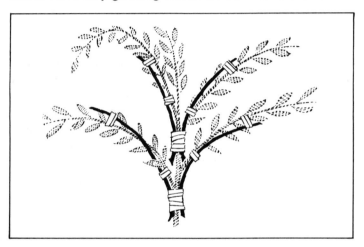

■ To adapt a field planter for small amounts of seed when planting the family garden, make a small hopper to fit inside the regular hopper. With this arrangement, all seed are available to planter plates and none is thrown around bottom of the planter boxes when plates start turning. A 2-pound coffee can with bottom and top removed is about the right size hopper to use with small plates; a 3-pound can is about right for larger plates, such as are used to plant peas and beans. A burlap bag stuffed around the substitute hoppers keeps them centered over plates. There is nothing to screw or bolt into place, and it is easy to change plates.

■ Breaking up clods and leveling rows in the garden is one job you can do easily with a tool built from an old reel-type lawn mower. To build it, take the reel out and slip it into holes at bottom of handle where mower was fastened.

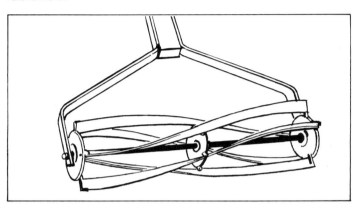

■ Inspection hole cover of poured concrete can be made easily for septic tank cover by using a dishpan. Place pans in cover form where inspection holes are wanted, then fill pans and cover form to same depth. Handles can be fashioned from rod or cable.

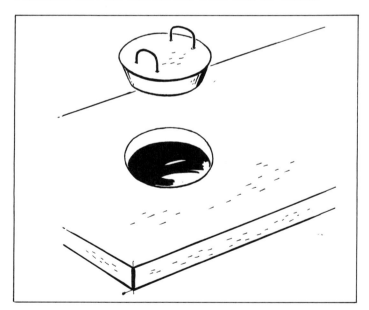

■ Use an old corn sheller to pulverize barnyard fertilizer for flowerbeds or small gardens.

■ For that home tomato garden, avoid the daily bugaboo of pruning and staking individual plants by spending a couple of hours building a portable "trellis table."

Each table is built of treated 2 x 4's bolted and braced. The tabletop is covered with welded wire. Size of table is 12 x 4 feet. Legs are 30 inches high. Each table accommodates six tomato plants in heavily fertilized soil. As plants grow, cotton cord is tied to stems until they grow through the wire mesh and support their own weight.

This method saves tomato fruits from rot, pillbugs, and varmints. Plants shade ground and reduce weed competition. Another advantage of table trellis is that it can be easily moved about garden so that tomato rows can be rotated annually.

■ Old lawnmower chassis can be used for a hose cart and garden cart. A piece of 3-inch strap iron bolted to the back of the mower base will hold the reel bracket. The reel can be turned to one side to leave space for a garden basket or box on the chassis.

■ Three metal coathangers, each bent into a U shape, and a plastic bag set over tomato plants lets you set out plants about two weeks earlier than usual. Clothespin or rubber band holds bag together at top. Cover it with soil to hold it in place at bottom.

When there is no danger of frost, loosen top and let bag drop to ground. When frost threatens, you can still raise plastic and tie in place over wires. Two bags instead of one will protect against severe cold.

■ Make this transplanter by removing the bottom of a straight-sided can. To use, place it over the plant; push it down below root level and then lift. When soil moisture is right, the plant and earth around it come up and are easily set in the new position.

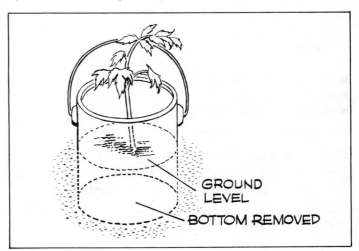

GROUND LEVEL

BOTTOM REMOVED

■ Use paper soda straws as packages for saving small seeds. On the side of the straw, write the kind of seed and the date stored. Twist one end closed, pour in seed and twist other end closed. Store "seed sticks" in jars for next season.

■ Garden tractors or horse-drawn garden tools can be used for putting down liquid chemicals that control nematodes. Container for liquid, with petcock at bottom to control flow, is fastened to bracing between handles of the plow. It holds about 1 quart and was made by shaping and soldering a piece of galvanized metal. Copper fittings and tubing are used to funnel material down to furrow.

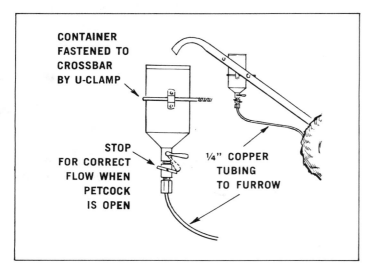

CONTAINER FASTENED TO CROSSBAR BY U-CLAMP

STOP FOR CORRECT FLOW WHEN PETCOCK IS OPEN

¼" COPPER TUBING TO FURROW

■ An old tire casing makes a good hose holder. It can easily be rolled from place to place. A G78-14 tire will hold as much as 75 feet of garden hose.

■ A dimestore plastic shoehorn makes a good tool to use in seedling boxes. The two different-sized ends are perfect for thinning out or transplanting.

■ Light, easy running, finger-tip control—that describes this handy yard cart made from a pair of discarded bicycle wheels. Secret is in the "yoke" or fork into which the wheels fit.

■ Renovator for lawn or small pasture can be built from old water tank. Teeth for this one came from old mowing machine. Hitch is built of scrap metal. Axle should go all the way through tank, which can be filled with rock or concrete for more weight. Knife bars from cutter bar of mower are placed every 6 to 8 inches around tank. These are attached to brackets or bolts welded to each end of tank so they can be taken off when tool is to be used for roller. If knife bars are not available, section of mower knives can be fastened to angle iron instead. Knives also can be welded instead of riveted to insure against loosening.

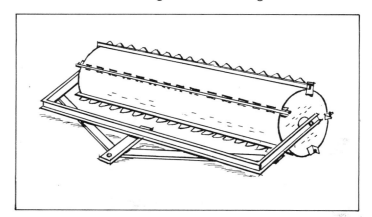